tHE
SUB

tHE SUB

A NOVEL BY

JIMMY JAZZ

INCOMMUNICADO PRESS

P.O.BOX 99090 SAN DIEGO CA 92169

©1996 Incommunicado Press
Contents ©1996 Jimmy Jazz

ISBN # 0-884615-15-5
First printing.

Cover and book design by Gary Hustwit. Cover photos by Patrick Haley.
Edited (sort of) by Gary Hustwit and Sandra Zane.

Thanks: Angela, Ashley, SeyMour, Shindig, Cecil, Mom, Dad, their spouses, Kristin,
Gary, Sandra, Tamara, Stampone, Michele, Pam, Eric, Chase, Bob, Paul, Byron, Liz,
Dawn, Nancy, Joe, Mick, Paul, Topper, Tom, Tim, Harlan, Corey, Elisabeth, Juliette,
Richard, Creedle, Bukowski, my students and…

Printed in the USA.

For the Visiting Teachers

the sub

Call me sub-human. I am a glance, a chance, a roll of the dice. A type. I have no story, no history, and most important—no future. Disconnected bullet train, pretty face, blue eyes grey skies, truth? lies? I am a memory of bad breath or shoes, good shoes, *In*-shoes. Minor hip hop *in* shoes. Diggy dig those punk rock rebel shoes. He must be cool if he's wearing those shoes, no rules, no blues, no dues, abuse. Cute too. You look like Luke P. Luke who? Sideburns. Kill your television. "Mr. Elvis. Mr. Elvis." So young, handsome, are those your real eyes? Are your shoes real? Do you really have a daughter? Do you really want to be…a teacher?

The reality check is now over. Verdict: Unreal, nonreal, a-real, sub-real. Reel to reel roll that real again Fred.

Five a.m. asleep in my head, with wicked human dreams about a girl, a train, and a bed. The phone is jangling, or does it buzz before the sun? The roulette wheel is spinning like the chamber of a gun, click click clack. Ghetto! Barrio! Slum? Socio, low-socio don't say lo-socioeconomic underpriviledged mum. Gum under the desk is my fault. Paper wrappers rapping rapers no new capers to waver.

Each day it is more difficult climbing out of bed. My pit deepens. Today I might not make it to my assignment. It is warm under the covers, cold up there, out there. Screw it all, I'm staying home. Agghhhh. Damn. My little daughter had climbed into bed with her sleeping mother and myself around four a.m. Her breath sawing at the morning silence. Shh shh shh shh shh shh. She is the vision of perfection, cheeks smooth soft pink rubber (I love to mush my face into hers when she's sleeping)—yet they are needy, hungry cheeks—probably wouldn't grow up sane if we lived on the street. I stretch one foot up to the floor, a heavy drudgery sledge hammer gravity pulling at the sore muscles in my neck and tired back. My sinuses are clogged with snot. I strip naked trudge down hall shoulder dragging hall wall. I catch myself staring into nada space. I have to force my getup on. It is that ridiculous. No matching socks. Another work day etched in the stone prison wall.

In class last Thursday a kid, a face without a name, a Mexican (more about the race problem as we proceed), a writer, a tagger, a slagger, a slacker lipsticks up his palm and smears it in some dope's mug. Okay. Funny. Ha ha. Sit out. Chill down, that's it you're done. And then he erupts, throws up, begins to spout shout and real hateful lava words fling in little drops and sear and cause pain and fear and I begin to shake like an aftershock. FuckFuckFuckFuck CluckCluck CluckCluck cluck, he said. Did I fail to understand his needs, did I say get up or grow up or shut up? No, I said please sit down. I carried it home and now mule-back full sack packing to work through heavy grey fog morning.

I walk into a classroom alone to face hair neck chest arms legs and feet thirty anatomies an hour. No names faces look the same all know the game. You think I am I think you is lame, shame, to blame.

Seating chart is like a treasure map covered with 'X's. So I just start digging, gigging, following the plan, acting like the man, counting the money. I make bubbles, a bubble means trouble. I'm over here, drinking a beer, I should be over there, alert and aware. Johnny's not here, jail, too much bail, I think he killed a cop. Me, I'm new, fresh from the zoo, stabbed the history keeper in the leg. I don't have a pencil product of a stencil. My notebook?

This is the plan. Today I'm the man, open to page one ninety-two. Turn, write Big ONE NINE TWO numbers on the board, and then picnic as books shuffle and chatter ruffles and they be digging in the book bags. Voila: gym sweats comic books handguns condoms pecans macadamia nuts berserking screw nut bolts and jolt cola spilling in sticky piles. Fifty-seven seconds later, What page? 192, more shuffle—keg party—kissed who—pimp slap the bitch—what page? 192 tick tock quick trick brick stack, a tennis ball bounce bounce bounce out of book hole slow roll under desks, crossing floor collecting eyes as it picks up momentum. What page?

sub two

One day I get the call to go back to my alma mater. It looks like the same suburban penitentiary—rough grey walls, slits for windows, 15-foot fences, barbed wire, cell block numbers, the warden in his suit, keep off the grass, walk to your class, shuffle ball chain like cons, move between the bells, the uniforms have changed but they're still the same. The guards look older. I'm still not one of them.

I went here. "That's nice dear. Go to room 203." The kids march in, we never looked so young—giggle chewing gum. Should I tell them how we tried to crawl through the air conditioning duct for no reason save to do it, or how we wanted to lay real grass turf in Obie's class, or how we plotted and searched the countryside for livestock to graze around her desk—a heap of sheep to beep or gaggle of pigs to oink. The senior class before ours put a fallen eucalyptus tree in her classroom. It smelled medicine fresh for months. The class before them set a dead washing machine on the porch, the class before left the burned-out hull of a Volkswagen. What have the classes since done to rival the sneaky genius of my way-hay days? What about the signs we hung on the staggering dizzy down precipice of the lockers questioning existence "WHY?" or the dead body outlines chalked along the walks? Surely there must be some legend left behind, some proof I been here before, under the floor, called on to read, stumbled over numbers, talking in class, circle jerking for big ass kickings, learning how to...what did I learn in high school?

A sub, A sub!

A shirt, no smock. Periscope up, depth charge deterrents at the ready, dive, dive, dive!

I went here. Where's Mr. Von Dyl? Do you think they would trust me with that sensitive information? Can I go to the restroom, can I use the library? May I visit my counselor? May I wander around the campus? Looking through the desk of one of my old teachers is like trying on my fathers discarded shoes, and they fit! No passes here, let me take roll, seat in your sits, don't throw a fit, I said park your zits. Who is not here? Please say here if here, not here if not here. What if you're halfway here, hiding in fear, illiterate or abused confused or using? Just grunt.

Today we read from *Romeo and Juliet,* by Willie McShakespeare. Please turn to page 74. "You went here?" Yes my dear. 1984. "You look so young, are those your real eyes?" Actually two of the fairest stars in all the heavens entreated my eyes to twinkle in their spheres until they returned. "What?" Page 74. Who wants to be Juliet? She's just a slut. And Romeo, just trying to bauble her hole. "You went here?"

Later, I jot over to the lounge eating a banana. Here my old teachers, stinky crusty creatures, make cave to denounce the system and let it be known to all how the years burnt their fuses and their career makes them pukish. Hi. "Can we help you young man?" Show me the garbage can. "You must be a sub?" Don't you remember '83 September I was enrolled in your algebra class. "Kids were a lot nicer back then." I exit.

The stone bench where I used to hang out between classes every day for years, the vital years, the nubile years, the nostalgic term, the stone bench is still here, still stone. African Americans now hang in front of the library bathroom where the blacks used to chill. My bench, the island bastion of minor too hip pre-punker and mod scenesters is now the roost of two Filipino girls. I sit with them, until they go off to class. Keroppi the nice frog box in tow. We don't exchange words. We don't even share silent reverence.

I'm supposed to teach p.e. but I don't have the key, and the gym doors are locked. I knock like a fool wake half the school but the door remains locked. I wander around the building, cages for gilding, sand on asphalt frictulating, basketball courts blazing, no sunglasses, no more hall passes, I wander, I wonder, I ponder asunder about slumber my head is throbbing skin cancer bobbing. A door, it's open, I'm in. I climb the stairs, nostrils aware, to the nest where the rare eagles perch. I can see all the naked boys from here like rodents to be swoopilated by gym whistle wearing pedophiles, I feel guilty about looking. I don't look any way but forward in urinals either. The walls are teeming with pictures of athletes gone by. Basketball teams, Vince, Pete, Mike. And newspaper clippings of Mike, and action shots of Mike, and Mike at home with his dog, and Mike winning the big game. Hey coach! "You the sub?" Yeah, I went here. "What year?" '84. "With Mike and those guys?" So the coach is a Mikophile, and I am now responsible for the return of seven basketballs. I'm wheeling the cart to the cage. Nike-shoed gods of rage steal the balls and run. A big spirit of '76 afro-boy mock pregnant b-ball in shirt bulging laugh-jogs to the bleachers. I give slow chase, walking at my pace and retrieve the ball in due time, but the others are gone bounced into the hoops by wild scattered youth, who is here, who is suited, who has run?

I taught gym other times. Some fine, some crime. Picture a weight room with two exits. Barbells, dumbbells. Cigarettes passing among the non-suits sitting on exit stairs. Every time I turn around two scamper through the damper. Two walked out. Their escape I hamper. "Warner's

around the corner." Like a fool I let them lock me out. I
should have ran around to the back door and caught them
bailing out, like a cartoon cat and mouse, why run when
you have their names? So I wrote a referral which said they
ditched, I left out the lock out.

One time I reported to the coach's office. Today I am
the athletic director, the man among men in the raw primal
sense. I am in the cage with the other coaches. There is one
Coach G.—six foot four inches tall, sleek and muscular,
young virile. He calls me 'coach' with a tinge of cynicism
which I may have self-invented from loin-ish feeling of in-
adequacy.

I don't speak coach. English major. (Rule: When in
doubt type yourself a rationalization.) I lost interest in
watching pro sports somewhere in teenagerhood (my dad
laments this as his failure grandé.) I lost interest in playing
sports later, though I still harbor affection for the beach
volleyball of my young manhood. I'm sure I could be en-
ticed into a good game with the right players. My friends
of yore and I coveted a sheer respect for the game itself.
Volleyball was the hub of our way of living. Beyond the
range of jock feelings. Hoo hoo. In it was a code to live by:
pure life appreciation. I value my playing of the game today
somewhat like I value baseball. I like nostalgic movies
about the game. (Slow hot kitty-box days of summer summon and resummon own nostalgic v.b. dramas on silver
head-screen.) I like to watch newsreels of Babe Ruth and

Ty Cobb. I derive joy from old radio broadcasts: 'The shot heard round the world.' I liked *Field of Dreams,* and *A League of Their Own.* There is one reality old-timer jock at Hoover, Booky. I love the name. He is loaded with stories about Ted Williams and the Brooklyn Dodgers. Though I can't talk with him either, I can listen.

For the most part my last years of college drilled, reamed, purged all spirit of competition out of me. Certainly I picked up an antipathy towards jocks, based on their anti-intellectual behavings. I think I've gotten over that. Lifting weights, lifting books: all the same to the worms. After high school graduation I lost also the opportunity to lift weights (I once benched 210 pounds) since visited by a slow loss of twenty pounds musculature (100 pounds bench capacity). I became a vegetarian after that and hence a further dwindle of carnivorous drives. So my time in the coach cage unable to speak their language was uncomfortable, and I probably fed their dislike of me with lost-wandering-in-dreams contorted facial expressions. I don't speak coach. Likewise am I unable to address a rowdy bunch of physical needy to be educatees.

My assignment second period was to monitor volleyball in the small gym. Volleyball, hmm? My sport. This should be great. I can show them how to bump, smooth set, and perhaps drill a few balls into the six-packed chests of selected wiseapples. No. I line them up for roll call and as I'm taking roll there is one kid swinging from the basketball hoop whoop-howling like jungle beast heated. And two guys are throwing tennis balls at each other. I have a whistle, brought half seriously, and I blow it frantically, no avail. Behind my back a few guys have taken the dinge-white V-balls out of the net sack. They are kicking them, full soccer-leg blasto into the walls. More tennis balls. Girls now too running, trying to peg boys. Innocents ducking, cowering. Balls zinging everywhere. Crossfire shootout of drive-by madness. There is Will who I know. He has a tennis ball poised in wild chase. Please don't throw those around Will. He looks at me. Lowers his arm. I am hit in the back with a tennis ball. I turn and put that one in my net sack. Hokey pokey turn myself around. Will has just thrown his ball. It goes wild off hitting some poor little victim skullways. I collect more balls as they roll near me. I keep them. The white balls are kicking around the gym. Here is Leonel. How's Betty? "She's not my sister." This has become a running gag between us. Betty is not his sister, same last name. Only I know Betty is pregnant (having seen her at grocery store.) A v-ball rolls up to him and he kicks it across the gym. Thump chaos of swirling dizzy madness. And there are bodies slipping out the doors. This is a distraction, a smoke screen for real ditch business. A girl is running after a guy, in and out of the people. He busts through double doors, bang! She pursuit. A minute later he bust through opposite gym door, she not losing not gaining. Whizzzz! She lets fly her ball. Miss above his head. Picked up and thrown by some other. The chase turns, they lap back the other way. White balls crashing with force off the ceiling. Loud slapping the walls. Tennis balls everywhere. Mad gibberish of squawk screams and yell laughs busying the mad rush of adrenal discord. I stop one little guy after he puts heavy foot to v-ball booting it across the gym. Why are you doing this? "No teacher." A tennis ball bounces up to my feet. I sack it. A guilty face youth hands me two balls he's collected. "I'm not part of this." And then someone yells, "Was that the bell?"

And the whole class, like the flush rush of a toilet pours through the exit door. They are outside, free. The oxygen fuels full voice yells and riot shouts of joy. They scream. This one kid, Tito, is doing flying karate kicks against the gym door. Bash. Slam Bang. His amigos begin to take turns. The castle is under siege! The battering ram BOOMS. "Ben's band bangs and Bim's band booms." I am moving to stop them. My voice unable to penetrate their mad quest from afar. Then. Clack, the door opens. There is a silver-haired coach frothing at the door. Fuming, ill-awakened dragon nostrils flaring. The soldiers laying siege panic and retreat running and scatter whooping in all directions. I am left alone holding my net sack of six volleyballs and now thirty-four tennis balls confiscated. She glares at me. She retreats to her gym chamber unsaid contempt hanging in the air about the battered door.

Another time we pushed the desks aside and put on a video aerobic tape. The girls followed the leader; the boys followed the girls. One pound weights dangling from seventh grade muscleless arms. I watch unable to jump to the rhythm. "Our teacher usually exercises with us." Nuff said.

English class, alma mater, in walks the security guard, the man, the fuzz, the pig, the narc, the bust, the thumb, the cuffs, the jail. He be Lee—fellow bench sitter and plotter of turfed classrooms, Scripps Pier surf ditchings, lunchtime beer guzzles, and Shaff cracker of elementary school park midnights of senioritis 1984. Lee. "Jimmy." The kids look at us as if we were the new untaboo homosexual lovers of graphic public displays of cuddle nozzle nuzzling human affection. Our parallel lives split apart like a country log, half to build a house half to fuel the fire. No distinction for who is which. Just different. No time for reunionizing, he has to take someone away, and I have a plan to man, a scam to sham, milk to deliver. Ain't seen him since.

sub three

"Hello young man." Hello Mrs. Principal I've got a great idea—she walked away in the middle of a thought that would have saved the rave, closed the shave, behaved the slaves. I need this job more than these couch lounge slobs (not gangsters of the blood variety). Will I become lounge sloppy when I grow up, someday, tomorrow, maybe, baby I've got rabies and I'm stark raving human can't you see? I bleed. I believe, I have energy and ideals underground. I'm the existential hero, I'm the clown. I'm the new Roman Nero, the school's less than zero, I'm renown. The poet of the know-its, the grombit of the graves the superstitious slanker of the toves. I rove across the county to classrooms of nil and bounty, kiss no booty, zooty suity kind and snooty to the masses in their ruffles I bring truffles of apricot cream. I esteem the highest dream that all who try can gleam along the seems of the ream of paper sheens, that glisten if you listen to the tassel hassle mission, I happy, I get sad, I stay calm when I'm mad. Whippee whoopee, grippee puppy, of the guppies hate the yuppies like the hippies, students drippy in their nappies with their sacky little wacky when they macky the happy tacky jerky off to worky join the turkeys in the season of paprika, Eureka! I've got it, Ah Ha, no that's not it, just keep crying tears are drying, I'm not, you're not dying so cheer up.

sub four

Advanced placement history. I haven't solved the mystery. "Some kids are smart and some kids are dumb, I don't pass judgement they're just having fun." This lyric is part of me, lodged in the heart of me, and now my job is to pass judgement. To sift, to weed out the unworthy, to tame, to conform, to socialize, to encourage, discourage, damn and direct, to pedestal, fight the bull, pull the wool, cull the skulls.

I must send them to college, to knowledge, just get them to show up to work on time. Tardiness is a sin. The lesson is those who don't conform are excluded from society. Please define the terms on the front board. The word hoard. Who the hell is Archduke Ferdinand? Chatter chat-

ter what's the matter, I thought this group was advanced?
"When we have a sub, we have a day off." Some calculate
calculus, some read *Gatsby*, some dole directions to parties,
"Should I work at Sea World as a whale?"

Four young lads in white skin clad call themselves the
eighties preservation society. They are trying to recall the
popular songs of the era. So I start to rattle some erudite
chattel about the songs I liked as a kid. I recalled the shows
I attended and the records in my rack scurfed with dust.
Three periods stand out, the first I'm ashamed to handout,
okay, 1980 I saw Van Halen at the Sports Arena, it stunk.
That was pre-*Jump* V.H. Yeah, David Lee Roth was jack
drunk on his ass, he couldn't remember the words to any of
the songs. It was boring, long didactic, I was wise enough
at 14 to know it. In those days I liked Aerosmith, Cheap
Trick, the fifteen minute songs of The Who. Then New
Wave happened in the popular culture. I loved Madness,
Joan Jett, X. The kids are laughing, sort smirking, like I'm
joking, you mean X as in unknown. I tried to name the
most popular groups, the ones who steered our thinking,
pocketed our love and our money. They wouldn't write half
of them down. They were preserving the pop culture of the
late eighties where their sixth grade brains were just begin-
ning to hear, tune in, the music that was always around
them beaming on the radio spectrum. My late eighties were
wholly obscurantist. I see that now, and relish worship it.
My senior year love affair with bands like the Clash, The
Jam, Dead Kennedys, The Specials launched me deep into
the heart of the local punk rock scene.

How could I begin to tell them about The Crawdaddys, The Penetrators, Battalion of Saints, The Wallflowers, Social Spit, Ministry of Truth, Diatribe, Insolents, The Front, Night Soil Man, all the local counterculture underground precursors of today's local pop culture.

I told them how I saw Social Distortion and The Red Hot Chili Peppers (big hip on the contempo-pop charts) in halls half the size of their classroom. They were impressed, were they impressed? I reclinered it all in philosophical teacher musings coming back to the point again and again that today's pop culture was yesterday's anti-rock. And if they turn over rocks in their own backyards they will find more than earwigs. They weren't ready. Time was gone. The bellwether was echoing in the hall, baaaaahhhh. Never pay more than seven dollars for any experience. A new group was filing in to the group filing out. A sub, a sub a day off.

I am cardboard, dart board, if I'm art board I'm blank.

Could I have everyone sit down please. Scatter, chatter shuffle weazle noozle feedle breed breed, cough, sneeze chatter wheeze shuffle snort. I send the evil eye lasering into the retinas of the gabby yappers. Mouths slowly close. Sit. (Punctuated with down pushing hand motions.) Sit. And I just stand like a lonely germ of silence, posture erect, steady ready. An epidemic of sitting. All now seated. Faces and hair. No two shades the same, beautiful, yet the same.

Chatter chatter, important matters "I got a date," "I lost my job," who did who? The eye pervades, but can't prevail. Then the big teacher voice steps out from the gut trying to squash the last straggle of conversation. I need two things, first to tell you to work on the definitions on the front board, second to take the roll. They freeze for a second, my eye locked in stare with thirty-four sets of soul windows, but the lights must be out inside because all I get is the reflection of myself. I can't hold so many eyes, and they drop off and become mouths and flapping tongues and intimate ears. I cruise down the seating chart bubble the bubbles, call the names, erase for students who are late or in the wrong seat. I alligator clip the attendance sheet to the door and seat quietly at the teacher's throne. I stare and pretend to write down names and throw out the eye which just boomerangs around the heads of my flock, annoying not to the point of deterrence. This period I just sit and stare and speak no other words. I make no human contact before the bell rings. I didn't even speak when Shalimar Zapp asked for a bathroom pass. I just looked at her and tried to see if she was a virgin or a dope fiend or an ace student or a bible thumper. I saw only my own reflection wavering in her eyes, handsome yet sad, like someone or thing I loved had died.

sub five

I was just thinking about this girl I used to have sex with when I was in high school, 18. I got a warm picture of her straddling me, her big breasts slopping all over my naked chest. The breasts were big and white, with blue veins running every which way, they were heavy and bruised easily. Thoughts drift back on to my first lover, tenth grade, 15. She 14, Juliet. We used to tie each other's hands with rope, and do whatever we wanted to each other. I remember having her bound and gagged in my best friend's bedroom and rolling deodorant on her thighs. It was a game to us. I would stick my penis inside her, and pull out and squirt clean semen on her little girl belly. It smelled like elementary school paste. We were blessed with the luck of stupid people, how she never got pregnant even once in the 166 times we did it, I can't explain. Stupid luck.

I can't talk to young people about this. I can't protect them with my experience even though the urge to swells up in my capillaries and reddens my skin. The school game is a lie. I can't tell them how my penis oozed the schmuck yellow guck of chlamydia. I can't talk about my friends who have had abortions—suffix 's,' that's multiple, pain anguish, fetus in the garbage bag pain with bleeding genitals. This desire to protect, this mother henism, doesn't think about the human nature, the monkey nature of thirty-three Curious Georges who must swallow their own puzzle pieces and break their own legs falling out of trees. There is no progress, only the repetition of the gene pool. No diving in the gene pool.

#6

Most of my students, my renta-students, come from far off lands bolstering their holsters with first languages not mine own. Their experience is different, they know nothing of American pop or book culture. There is no base to sculpt on. No ground to cultivate, no time to enculturate. Learning is like building a room addition. These children are nomads. No rooms. They are on the run, void of fun.

Kidisti footed the Sahara desert for eleven days without food to escape her country under siege. Anab, a Somalian Muslim, has fasted for twenty-seven days. She is failing her classes. Woozy. Hugo was carted off to Mexico in the night to work for his family. He will return weeks later, staccato education interupticus. Jennifer shares a room with two cousins and a baby sister. Homework? As I took roll today thirteen bodies were absent.

Pam is pregnant, Jamal the impregnator drunk on the roll for another skanky hole, mack daddy player a fly-girl slayer shooting for the freaks, with his sick truck speakers boomin' to the bass beat boogie of the streets. "Man, you try to go with a lot of girls, what is this third grade? You gotta fuck as many holes as you can." And he illustrates with feet planted spread and sine wave rolling across his body, hands planted on an invisible hump, pelvis the focal point pounding, Boom, chaka Boom boom boom.

sub six

"The kids from the streets are the kids that you meet." [1]
Another lyric. Music in my head. There was this kid from
Memphis who stood up in class at the goading and prod-
ding of his classmates. And he danced some wiggly gangster walk and spieled his musical talk, dubbed *The Lyrical
Drive By*. It was riotous inappropriate for our task, our
class...damn whatever we were supposed to be doing, I
wished I'd had a tape recorder.

Many have a cousin or friend gunned down, I read a paper about a caper where this kid opened fire with his
brother's .45. His homey was bleeding just barely alive. The

---

[1] Angelic Upstarts *Kids on the Street.*

Impala got away, he never saw their faces, or knew if he had killed.

I'm standing in front of class didacticating pronouncements of verbiphonic nematodes—POP, pop pop. Gunshots outside. Hit the floor! The kids are flying out the door. "I gotta go home, get strapped." If they come a shooting, we'll come a gunning. Panic, manic Hispanics in a panic, "OBS is moving on our town," the East D'ego crips coming gunning for our cribs tight lips no slips we'll gun them down. The principal's office sent a rumor control bulletin to every class with remarkable speed, announcing that the cops had arrested a developmental disabled guy across the street shooting bullets into the air, as if it wasn't polluted enough.

Graffiti. Taggers, humph. Can't they think of something new? They talk about art. I say, is writing your name on the wall art? Was the guy who wrote "Squirrel" on our coin-op washing machine an artist? They say, "Are murals art? Is Van Gogh art?" Fine retorts to my ill thought snorts. There was "Wepon" who invented his own font, he wrote my name in his twisted letters instead of reading, or journal writing. One day driving I saw "Wepon" written on the freeway overpass. I didn't see him that day to ask. There is a new language here. Tag names and gang signs. A new language is the seed of new thinking. Conjecture? More than hope I wish to help overcome the hostility, the anger, the violence. But I don't speak the language.

I taught fourth grade for three days. A new kid comes
in claims blood, at a crip school, he's a fool. The kids practice the new language during lunch. "This is the sign for
Brick Wall Piru, no that's a Samoan blood, is this Logan,
or Lincoln Heights?" "I don't know, but this is the crown of
the Latin Kings." We need to inject {+ - x ÷} with like mystery and power. So I do think teacher thoughts. I am closer
to teacher than ghetto gangster. Yip hop hurray.

There are little clubs, tagging groups, less than gangs,
who go writing in the nighting with Krylon do their paint-
ing. I ask why? They say "boredom" or "it's fun," on the run
from the man, with a can in their hand. The news says a
tagger shot a neighbor in the face on the street where I live
in the hood.

I remember when some gang from a different neighbor-
hood (bloods) attacked the school I was at that day's crips
on the Boulevard in front of the school. The school police
scrambled, the big police were called. A hundred bodies ran
to watch or jump in. Meanwhile I watched from the classroom steps as Victor explained how East Side seized the
moment, carpe momentum, to engage the Oriental Boy
Soldiers behind the school. That was the real battle he
claimed. Only those gangs had sufficient numbers to control the area, drug sales I figured. And then I felt really sad
hard empathy for these kids who are pawns in some deal-
ers, and smugglers game. Barrio soldiers. Dreadlock rasta.

I was at Roosevelt Junior High (Teddy or Franklin D. I dunno) supervising an after school carnival. I just wander through a sea of light and dark brown faces. No Asians here. They are integrated, laughing together, dancing, dunking teachers and tuxedoed security narcs into freezing water for ducats. Everything is happy. But then I notice the difference between African music and Mexican music. The d.j. is alternating the rhythms, but the dancers are segregated, separated, cliqued, gang sorted. Why didn't I see it at first glance? A comment sparks a push which croquet hammers into a shove bing bing bing. "I'm sitting here on this little yellow line/on the two lane hiway/ just trying to hitch a ride/ but no one is going my way." Thirty Mexicans line up with chests inflated in the North, thirty Africans line up in the South fists clenched. I am referee to a race riot. They are Americans, of Dodge City standoff streets. It actually is high noon. The cold war stares escalate, elevate, ladder ho, step up, move to the hills first with hostile language, same ole cluck cluck. And do I know how to control mobs? No. "Race riot, don't buy it." My lyrics, my own youth brawls no help now. The security narcs bust through the lines grab and drag the biggest guys from each side and the riot is over as quick as it began. Over, well? stalled, couched, curbed (moved to the sidewalk) the spontaneity has been vacuumed as sides plot to clash across the street in the grass. Young people running, huddling, wild talk jumping from body to body. Adrenaline rushing. The phone in action: "Older brother bring your homeboys and pick me up from school."

That night Roosevelt's banging made the news. Hey I was there, before the bloodflow, saw it coming, felt the drumming of the heartbeats, saw the buildup before the blow up, be back tomorrow to catch the gossip, help the mop up of blood on the campus lawn.

sub seven

The next day I'm forty miles east of the city streets, teaching farmers' sons to draft. They are learning to art the technical way, with proportion grids, triangles and squares. This classroom smells like my childhood. Mechanical pencil sharpeners, gumbi erasers, t-squares, soft and hard leads, the smell of adjustable art tables reminds me of dear old dad. It is Country Music Friday as opposed to Heavy Rock Thursday. The country boys like their music, which is difficult for me to relate to, grip, pallet, stomach, digest. "Can I take a leak?" Please don't take one, leave one. The fun's begun with hickoids throwing bits of eraser at each other when they think I'm not looking. "Sub day, free day." "I don't usually do any work." I usually fix up right in class, the teacher ties off the rubber for me. "I finished all my work yesterday, and I can't start a new project until Mr. Drafting gets back." Albert Lyons (an old friend, high school, met recently in the street between his folks' and my pop's house) claims he punched the drafting teacher at MMHS, 1981. Al claims to have "terrorized" substitutes. Country drone feeding slow pulse temple headache. Please, don't use the airbrush. "Did you hear about Chester?" What are you supposed to be doing? "Nothing." Country kids are having a grand time making beware of Chester signs. They employ goat and horse stencils. "We get upset when people mess around with our animals." I try to explain that herdsman have been getting their rocks rolling on the flocks ewing since herds became the word. The lonely shepherd in his midnight pasture fiddling. Nothing new. 'When men were men, and sheep were nervous.' 'Why do shepherds wear long flowing robes? Sheep can here a zipper a mile off...' There just happened to be goat stencils lying around? Any other school in this county, country music wouldn't be an option—Ranchero maybe. There's no angst in it, no rebellion, no joy. I like Hank Williams Sr. Johnny Cash wrote some cool songs. But *Achey-Breaky Heart?* What are you supposed to be doing? "But Chester mounted our sheep." I should have known as I past the rodeo arena. Slow drone headache rolling, this is boring it's still morning.

At lunch I'm alone. I fetch a cassette from my car and serve myself a healthy dose of Stiff Little Fingers screaming bit of noise on the country music classroom hi-fi. I'm in heavy identification with war on the Dublin streets. *Barbed Wire Love.* "I'm out of sheep what should I do/ I'm out of sheep/ might as well mount ewe." SLF brings the connecting childtime lyrics. Two students come for lunch and get excited about the music. Hey, it's nothing new. Just SLF available at a record and even CD store near you. He writes the name on his notebook. Hey write down Rhythm Collision, and Cadillac Tramps and a thousand other of the greatest bands in the world. Do I have time to share all the music that I love? This is the kid to do it with. He is no *Blackboard Jungle* swinger who will smash my disks like frisbees while I suffer, while I crumble in the rubble, "it was love at bomb site." But the bell rang, BRRRANG!

I thought I had better get the punk rock off and the country music on before the place goes pogo wild flipping off the handle, "When in Rome do as the Vandals." With the new set of the same old tricks, "Can I go to my locker?" "I don't work." Don't touch the airbrush, Chester is nothing new. The head pain dives into the stomach, gravity, nausea, swirl, churn, spurn the twisting worm. In walks a student with a seven-gallon hat, rodeo prize belt buckle to match, heeled boots, and he spits his chaw in the waste basket. I almost bust a spleen trying to hold back a hearty, lungy, belly laugh of guffaw hee haw stereotype hell. I contain myself and say Howdy, and welcome and sit down, and toss his late pass in the trash with the gob wad of tobacco spew.

On the long stretch of road home I play the stereo for what it's worth, "Break out and leave this life behind." This music was made for long bends in the hiway and the wide open gut of the big sky horizon leading to the great unknowns of vast America. I am free, a condor on the wind, unwinding the twisted gnarl of lies that is the workaday, twisting it into the truth of happy home with books and music and kisses from my daughter and her mother. And I can fart, or burst out in song, unlimited, boundless, anything goes, everything is permitted. The superficial world of fake fronts falls to the asphalt, loosing the feeling that breathing is natural. I can curse or praise beauty, I can masturbate into the acrylics and paint the sky.

sub eight

The next day it is South to the border. Cafeteria serves Taco Bell insults. Sometimes, if I'm desperate mad hungry I'll eat a bean burrito from T.B. Usually I'd rather have t.b. than eat at T.B. but if I go through the school day without eating I always acquire the throbbing temples. I must leave the sacrificial aspirin at the temple. I have my own bottle of 300 tablets, generic. When it is empty, that will mark 150 headaches, 150 headaches, 150 headaches too many.

I am seldom organized enough to pack a lunch. Bare pockets, nair cupboards, empty stomach. Breakfast is beyond my power so usually I fast. Luckily I'm jazzed by Hesse's *Sidhartha* samana and can transcribe my hunger into spiritual experience. Even if I have a few dollars I would rather buy a used paperback lit, something permanent forever than a peanut chew and yogurt. Sometimes I get free soda crackers and salad dressing for go energy to get me home, where waits peanut butter and jelly on tortilla. My Spanish speaking compadres are shocked and amazed that I would slander their culture with peanut butter tortillas. This is poet on the go food. And free espresso from Angela[2] (daughter's mother who I share life and bed with) keeps my eyeballs jingling into the night and adrenaline keeps my fingers tapping the keys. My leg shakes when I write. I've seen kids do the same in the class, eyes clamped with iron thought clamps to the paper. This is when I get excited.

The first question down south is usually, "Do you speak Spanish?" I usually reply, "No hablo español," which reeks with oxymoronic zit removal power and suits my arms and shoulders fine. If I fail to say I know a few key words the next thing I hear is pinchi chingada this, chupa mi verge that. The guys will usually clue me to a cackle of feminine gibe, "They're talking about how cute you are man." Thanks ese. What does one say? Sometimes I fix the eyes on them like I really know what they are saying, till they gush blush, and cringe embarrassed burst to giggle.

---

[2] A teenage student high school girl or two asks me every day if I'm married. Sometimes I say yes, sometimes no. Technically I'm not but spiritually I am—married. When I say "together eight years," she wants to know our story. Part of this story is told in another book: *House of the Unwed Mother, HUM* for short.

The classrooms here are surprisingly the same as those in the far hickville east. The skin shades are paler out there, but the thoughts, the surface behavior remarkably similar. There is a terrible racist myth being perpetuated by the teaching class—i.e. that these brown kids should be any more interested in literature by Rudolfo Anaya, Gary Soto, or even Oscar Hijuelos[3], than white boys are excited by Hemingway, Hawthorn, Faulkner, Steinbeck. There is no automatic interest by women in Alice Walker and Gwendolyn Brookes nor does Langston Hughes strike instantaneous orgasms at the sounding of his name and color in the black male. "You can't be bored by this he's a black man like you." You schmoo, hoo doo voodoo guru of new glue spew queuing to chew blue jews doo doo.

I was monitoring art class at Palomar high. A tough place if you listen to the lounge prattle. One teacher rattles about the recent Bonita mall battle. A Mexican shot an African in the face near the food court. (Trying to impress the Hot Dog on a Stick girls.) Teacher X sites the assailants name and Teacher Y pipes up, "Yeah he was one of ours." "Most of these kids carry guns." "Not to class though, most of the guns are in the parking lot." Palomar is a continuation exception to the rule. 'Danger, danger Will Robinson.' I found the students better behaved than most. They were cool, last chance cool, and what I can't stand is silly. I'll take the true hard case over silly any day. That's just me though.

---

[3] *The Mambo Kings Play Songs of Love* being one of my favorite books. Not yet in a classroom near you, ¿maybe soon?

The silly ones have cussed me out, and sent me home with stress bearing burden so heavy I snapped at my little one for acting like-silly. I'm sure the hard one would just shank me if it came to that, and I'd be dead and wouldn't have to worry about writing a referral.

Most of the art in art class was bullshit. The kids mindlessly cranked out project after project without any feeling. Like killing on t.v. Just follow the steps 1,2,3 this project's dead, only to appear on a different show next week. There was one girl, my heroine, who just got out the paints and made a little love note for her boyfriend code name: Snoopy. She got real flinging Jackson Pollock with it and was having a fine time smashing her frustrated love onto the paper. Until, dun dun dun! She specked a fleck of paint on an African's white tank T, and he called her "a god damned fucked up slut whore and bitch." Which I'm sure Snoopy heard about with later news fodder repercussions, dig the boom boom.

It reminded me of the time me and a fellow European (he a middle European and me a northern European) were tossing his football down the street and it flew awry rolling up the drive kissing the Caddy tire. And this seen by the sons of the Caddy owning daddy, led to a one hit brawl, my pal's mouth filled with blood, and ten other Africans, friends from grade school, Lonnie B. who's been to my house many times among them, laughing like a bunch of crows. And John went down with his hand a bowl of blood and tooth soup. He tried to crawl under the turf and vanish. And me holding the ball, shaking, ready (yeah right, looking for an escape route) to hold off any sort of gang jump. The guy who busted John's grill was maybe three years and a foot taller than him, which helped to permanently impress the scene upon my psyche. Life is not fair. The ghetto kids know this, the fat second mortgage lounge squabbling teachers know but often forget. They forget that their job, our job, is to educate all, any way we can if the pupils will dilate for it or not.

When I say the ghetto kids know that life isn't fair I liken them to the addict who knows that alcohol or cigarettes will kill him. Is the drowning man's last thought a regret for not taking swimming lessons? The ghetto kid knows that you can get out of poverty via education, and they know that the odds are against. They have no concrete success model to model, no yellow brick road to the ivy league. Violence, death, prison pattern, of Matterhorn line standing "climb to the top of the slide, and then you go for a ride till you get to the bottom where I see you again"[4]—generation reincarnation again and again and again.

Still, I'm a no air in the tank submarine cruising on the surface of the ocean. Sonar and radar bouncing back the geography of personages. The minds are mines. No port in sight and the enemy is all around.

---

[4] The Beatles *Helter Skelter*. Coming to me via Siouxsie and the Banshees.

sub nine

Special Education. There is a computer, name's Sams, that dials my number every morn or eve between 5:30 and 9:30 with an assignment. I always take the first job that calls cause I need the money, the dough, the bread, the spread, the loot, the kaboodle. The first job is usually Special Education. SED (Severely Emotionally Disturbed or Social-emotional difficulties) PH (physically and mentally handicapped) LH (learning disabled.) The classes are always small in number, and there is always an aid. God save the aid. Especially Sid the aid at Kearny: true Now-saint of god patience and cool soul. Sid who told me story, laughing at the absurdity of it all in retro-inspection, of two special lads. One angry cooling down outside looking in the window. The other making taunt faces safe inside ha ha happy.

And lad outside throws his hands at the neck of the taunter right through the window glass, smash. The crash of blood and screams. "I seen a lot of wild shit."

I mentioned before my experience teaching fourth grade. I left out the fact that both the teacher and the special aid for this class experienced heart failure on the same weekend.

Locked in the looney bin with frothing foaming maniacs, shoving knocking teeth loose, chair throwing, desk clearing psychopaths. I can still see them in absurd repetition watching the 101 dalmatians watching t.v. The dog of fo god, oad the eht dao evil live bananagram. And the subaid was the craziest thing I've heard. She would explode with them, "shut up you fucking little shit," and the kid would flail kick and fog snarl at the root canal of injustice. She was big and held him down till he stopped kicking and screaming like those chloroformed corpses in the espionage movies. There was one girl who provoked this little crazy boy into nearly killing her. I could barely restrain him. I couldn't drag him to the office. He squirm kicked and pulled and flailed and snarl jawed and spit and rabid wild foamed out storm floods of puke spit hatred. He strained all my muscles. If I let him go he would have snapped her neck or harvested her corn rows by the roots, he would have threshed her wheat so to speak. He was a dirty little bugger. He wore the same dirty clothes both days he showed up that week. A big brown chocolate stain on once white blood drive T-shirt. What could I possibly know about him? This was a week of screamers. I know that these kids don't make it.

The next week I was monitoring S.E.D. at M.M.H.S. where only the calm ones with good meds made the grade with shade to spade, dig. Everything was quiet. Where were the screamers, the unexorcised demons? I preached history, they took notes and listened.

The middle school as the name decries was half as nutty as the primary booby hatchet, with variant nurse Ratchets tightening the shock clamps of disciplinary society stamps.[5] S.E.D. at Keiler Middle was a typical ringer dinger, or was it an atypical dinger ringer? The aide here was strong and calm, a blessing, another saint. She had her own problems: a man at home down with "sugar" loosing his toes to gang green, long bus ride to and fro in the heat and cold of night and morn. She liked to whisper. "We don't let this one alone. He eats lunch in here with me. No mainstreaming for him. He will do anything the other kids tell him. He lit himself on fire. That boy over there made him go down." Wait. This kid forces another kid to suck him off and he still goes to this school, this is common knowledge in the gossip ears, and he is sitting there two desks away basing on the poor sap tapper?

---

[5] Stop right here and see *One Flew Over The Cuckoo's Nest,* if you haven't already.

At Bell junior high there is a kid who thinks he is a bus. That is what the aid told me. He seemed normal enough to me. He feels safe in this room she says. He was goofing around like any kid. Then I saw him on the campus weaving in the traffic of the student body madness. He was shifting gears, and emoting air brake and horn sounds. Scary real bus sounds. His mom was a crack addict. When he was three she got on the bus with him in the mornings and ditched him at the first stop. He rode the bus all day and she would pick him up at the last stop. He becomes a bus as a defense mechanism. The mind is an incredible thing. Next year they are cutting the special day classes and floating him out in the mainstream, no doubt he will drive out of the lake with water streaking down the windshield of his big mack bus.

I met this spec. ed. kid at M.M.H.S. He told me about this band he wants to join and showed me a Metallica video, just the bass solo which he can now play. All is not lost.

At Clairemont high[6] I met a wonderful set of people. I can't remember all the names, lost in the bombblasted nomenclature of my sub mind. These kids were getting

---

[6] This same day the death of my dear friend Don Thorpe, a teacher at Clairemont high was confirmed for me. I had tried to go shopping for him a month before, but he refused to see me, "too weak." He died riddled with cancer. I met Don in a writing class in 1985. We took our first screenplays to register at the writer's guild, lunched at some upper crust Hamburger joint, and shopped on Rodeo drive—as all good movie moguls should. He wrote a decent script about a homicidal comforter which may or may never get out of pre-production.

R.O.P. training to be food service workings, cogs in the grog nog. In the morning I rode with the first group on a shiny yellow school bus into the downtown. We stopped at the Goodwill where these kids worked. Pushing brooms, wipe ragging the tables, and arranging the salt shakers and mop waters. They learned to punch in and out by the clock, the meaning of an hour—four dollars twenty cents. They became can stackers and dish rackers. David was the king: a smiley ringy ding on the cold cash machine. He was entrusted to the register to monitor the cash flow. He collected the quarters for the coffee, the dollar for the danish. David was special and got to skip school for an extra shift. He liked me, and we became comrades on the bus ride, friends really. I spent most of the hour helping a young lady with her food handler's exam practice. I read directions and she searched the word searches, in between she smirched the big purchase, schmoozled and bamboozled, to a worker gave her number, he was to call at three. The Goodwill was a downtown rickety clank of a building with services serving and thriftiness for the yes and non deserving. Deep in our hour the elevator shafted stuck shut with rang jangling alarm scramble of granite panic slate of emergency. A lad alone in the deep rocket hole bowel of creaky cobweb dark. Minutes passed like nervous heartbeats and beady sweat balls bounding off the plaster karmasaurus disaster skeleton of the illwill chill of sunless frill grills killing hope. The elevator began to creak and rise like vomit launching anticipation. The door opened. A Goodwill worker of calm collected nerves strolled out, he was on the clock so everything was okay, peachy, smooth, dandy like candy in the handy spandex.

The bus ride home lulled one of our young workers completely asleep. His head jerking wildly like the ghost rudder of a storm tossed ship. And sea salt spray gurgled from his lips over bow and brow and the eyelid sails were full of rapid dreams. I watched him, and took the long middle passage back to seventh grade. I had just gotten out of the hospital, neck still snapped like dry twig crack. Healing, but still like tacky glue. If I wanted to attend junior high I would have to ride the bus with the serious no control over function drool and groan squad. They spit and smelled like dirty diapers. I can still hear the animal 'oans wailing up into the bus rafters like hungry fingers digging through carrion for some nutritious connection with the starry pantheon of human feeling. And I too served time in a special education class, adaptive p.e. for the severally lame and uncoordinated. I was the "star athlete," immobile neck contraption of limited vision and close to zero function clunking. We played Frisbee golf. I can't summon even a face of that sentence, I served my time and got out alive, unreamed at the seams.

The second crew suited up for Sea World and they had trouble with the dressing curtain falling, and boy and girl mauling all in fun. There was one kid who was saving his money to buy a Harley Davidson motorcycle. He was a beautiful male specimen, o.k. q.t. G.Q., trouble speaking, the silent movies would have served him well. At Sea World I took in the shark encounter and checked out the walrus tank. The male and female walrus were churning circles around the pool. The male would turn on his back and give the tourist gawkers a big show of real animal kingdom penis. A foot thick! He was masturbating with them, no question. He repeated the pattern eight, ten times while I watched, penis up only as he passed the people, each time I expected a huge white wad to spring forth and spider cling to the Japanese camera thing.

sub ten

I'm subbing at Keiler Jr. High in a basic living class. Washing machines, ovens, sewing machines, color t.v., refrigerators, super bastion of modern convenience. Teacher may not know these kids iron their clothes with 1905 iron heated on the stove top. Two lads are sitting across a table, slouch slumped in a posture only good for laughing. A kid sat in the middle of them keeping score with hash lines in the twenties already on both sides. "Your mother's big black lip flaps so much they hung her on the flag pole." "Your mother's booty was so big black and stinky..." ping pong ding dong pimp slap. If they could make the guy in the middle laugh, they earned a point. Forth and back one after another. The kid in the middle laughed at every debasement with "black" in it. The darker the hardy har hardier. I heard this guy on NPR talking about his job as consultant to the *Cosby Show*. Bill wanted to make sure that none of the jokes, gags, pranks or yokes were based on put down humor. He paid these guys a couple of hundred grand a year to X out the derogatory yaks.

A little brown sparrow of thin fine marrow flapped into class one day. Up jumps Gerardo, and Hugo to slam the damn windows so the bird had no place to go. They chased it over desks all around the room, it was flapping in a panic beak bent manic. I opened the window, someone closed it. Finally, the window opened the bird flew free past the trees into the breeze. Would they've put salt on its tail, had they caught it? ¿Eaten it?

Ninth grade Humanities class.[7] Here there was a young lady with terrible acne. A poppy field of pussy headed zits. It was hard to look at her. Three guys in the class drew a left brain picture, a stick girl with nappy hair and triangular waves of zits. Plus a cartoon speech bubble crying, "I'm not a freak." This may sound like a typical cruelty, until these boys bring the picture up to me and say "Does this remind you of anyone?" and point at their victim. I have no patience with those who try to lure me into cruelty. I quietly crumpled the paper and said nothing. They wanted me to cause a scene. They wanted their slander broadcast big media flash hurtful. I noticed after class they retrieved their trash, and delivered it to her person.

---

[7] And me out of school holding English degree unable to teach this combination English/ Social Studies class.

This was not the first time students assumed I would join forces with their misanthropy. I don't remember where it was that two guys approached my renta-desk in a lull moment and men to man said, "Hey did you notice there were a couple of beached whales in here?" Nudge and wink with a snicker over shoulder. I lost it. You and you sit down in opposite corners and I don't want to hear another word out of either of your mouths or I'll have you suspended! Full volume, no problem, did I cure them? Were they victims, programmed by the t.v. and the ad mag manikins of plastic body skinny thighs, melon breasts and buttless, brainless, stainless, veinless, gainless boop boop pee dupes?

And then there is the mysterious punishment inflicted on the receivers of decent grades. "Miss straight A's." "No! I got one C." She spit sputters all a-fluster to buster with the mustard. Why is school so uncool? I suppose there is a point when institutional education becomes didactic twaddle. The hippest people I know are the graduate school dropouts. The Nirvana seekers, the poets, the philosophers, the scholars. The learning process isn't dead for them. I don't think I have respect for any one who resists learning with the excuse that his or herself is too dumb, stupid, moronic, dullard, nitwit, numskull, airhead, ditz, dolt. They may be, but that's not an acceptable excuse in my book. We can all learn something especially from misfits, fools, jesters, clowns, naives, innocents, and virgins. In this time frame the true rebel is the smart sober atheist virgin.

The masochism help bubbles of drowning men on sinking ships dip the trip to the surface of the lip. Students tell me odd things. Rodel, ROTC, PEON explains how a new rank or medal is tacked on in the corps. The spiky metal spear pin medal lance is impale pounded to flesh chest by each member of the troop. To advance is to hurt. The further the advance, the worse the hurt. Bobby corroborates. He will hire himself as a mercenary to the highest paying country. The U.S. Marines don't get to kill enough. He is in training to resist loose talk under torture. His mother subjects him to electric shocks. Bobby saw a boy machine-gunned down for throwing rocks at a military guard post. He has broken his legs jumping from aircraft, his arm was recently busted in a piru/crip football game. Bobby has eaten human flesh at his uncle's mortuary. He claims to get drunk with the unit commander. He is 18. He has been married and divorced. His mother has cancer of the gut, whiskey rot. Bobby spends hours pent in small ill lit room smoking and drinking with her. He has lived and wishes to die. He delights in disgusting his classmates, disrupting their ease, fecal breeze of loose disease sneezing through the brown bare branch winter trees, and busted knees.

sub eleven

Rodel works at Pizza Hut. I worked at Pizza Hut back in high school days. I don't say we called it Pizza Slut, or Pizza Rut, because mine is the image of the content, happy worker, work smirk and whistle through the briar and the thistle, eating gristle ducking missiles, and at Mid-winter-time sucking face under the mistletoe. We share a jargon. We both know how many pepperonis should lay on a large pizza. I relate stories about the heavy mixing blades of the Hobart dough mixer and he nods. This is his life story too. I tell him about the gnats that would get caught up in the whirling batter, though I leave out the metaphorical connection between the gnats and the minimum wage laborers. I follow that story with another about a rite of passage. To be a cook, to be a cook among men high esteemed, one had to snap into the dough between the clashing blades and snatch a piece. This comes straight out of tagging your enemy on the battle field and palomino galloping away alive. There was a lady, older, a little slow of thought, who tried her skill. Her arm was crooked in the churning hook, when she looked pain glossed her brow. The Hobart snapped her arm, wrenched it wick-wacky cat out of the sticky sack— eee heee hee.

She tried to sue Pizza Hut and ended up fired, canned, put out, booted, sacked, dumped, ditched.

There was Marina and Esmerelda, twelfth graders, who sweated for the wage as Pizza Hut slaves. Marina described how Esmerelda added meaning to the make table with her fiancé after hours. And I recalled my friend Herbie (cook) who piled over Buffy (waitress) on the boxes of frozen cheese in the shallow freeze. I recalled this odd thought, though related it not.

And Saul, pronounced with a soft teeth saw and an ool as in pool. Saul worked at Jack-in-the-Box. He worked to feed himself, and was fired for eating a hamburger.

I run on I run in to hundreds of kids who work after school at McDonald's, Burger King, Carl's Junior and other fast food rackets, jacked up establishment neo-slavitude sweat grease and zit factory of the service working class part-time hospital-impossible poor. As I wake them up in class I tell them all, quit your job. Live! Be young without money. "But I can't pay car insurance, and car repair, and registration fees, and time in line at DMVs without my job. I need my car to get to work."

The clinch, the flip, the rotation motivation inclination station, like the Hatians: "I love working at Carl's Jr., it's better than being at home."

sub twelve

Homophobic robots of the neopersecution rabble strike fear in the loins of the grabass queers trying to function as consumers, eaters and feeders, not breeders but raisers sharp as teeth. Most kids are not sophisticated enough to identify sexual preference via countenance. A friend, a fellow sub, less than human like us all, liked to arm wrestle his students for control. He wins (always did) they had to do the assignment for the day. They didn't know he was as queer as the sunset. I had met his husband. In the lunchroom he talked about good sweaty monogamous sex that wore him out, tired through his muscles, without sleep. Those boys held hands with a faggot, a rump ranger, a fudgepacker, fart farmer, turd burglar, colon cropper, gonad gargler, rectum rifler, a fairy, a poof, maricon, puto, joto, homo...and all the ugly words which are the first insults out of their mouths in the halls against the ears, strong words trunked in fear.

I always turn Manzinar and *The Crucible* towards the AIDS epidemic. I can see this country rounding up the gays and lesbians in a big camp and holocausting them. I see it in the hate-trained spectacles of tomorrows sorrows.

I masquerade as people of all shapes, sizes, ages, rages, turning pages of the mages, both sexes, all preferences; I pose as teachers young and old. Many times I find students giving me the opinion of their teachers. I don't like Mr. L. Why not? "He's a little faggot man." Well, what if he was (he is)? "Well, he picks on people in class." He is hated, but he's human. I am loved at, gawked over and whispered about and I am a specter, a shade, a shadow of antimatter.

"That guy walks like a fag." "I saw you in a mag, smoking a fag, I saw you in a mag you were kissing a man."[8] Where is the threat. Have all these guys had their butts pinched and propositioned as I was at age 15? More girls for you Jack! Unless the fem-mass hips to the homo happening. I learned the other day that two women might possibly create a baby with science-combined eggs. They would have a girl child. Men become obsolete. I don't want to hear another derogatory note belch from your mouth. I love saying things like that. Though I feel guttural, low, sub-sub less than saint. Sometimes my exemplary example

---

[8] Wire *1,2, X U*

suit slips off and exposes the rotting corpse of my patriar-
chal cultural ornaments dangling with the burned out bulbs
of Pic 'n' Sav christmas lights from my worm chewed rib
cage.

sub thirteen

I am not a good liar. Kids ask questions. Kids are questions. Like nitroglycerine on the powder kegs of unstable government in the hands of greedy cabinet generals they wait to be ignited. A push from the left, a shove from the right. The questions snowball from general to bottom of the hill personal. I could not be a closet commie or queer. They would drag it out of me. Somehow TEACHER seems like it should equal celibate and sober. The snowball rolls with the same flaky questions picking up first, mostly, so that I started opening my act with a spiel:

Age: 26
Eyes: Blue
Child: One
Her age: 5

Her name: Anna, but she prefers Ashley. I call her Anna (soft A like tongue out aaaaah)

I just rifle rattle this info out, while juggling three nectarines.

Pop, poop pop pop. Hands go up, tiny voices chime in the round. "Are you married?" Technically no. "I'm available" (crouch giggle, crotch wettens.) Sorry, thanks, spiritually I am married. I live with Anna and her mother. Unmarried with child. "Why aren't you married?" Too trendy. "When was the last time you had sex?" Did you lick her bean this morning before work? Straight to the mundane, "Where did you get your shoes?" Dr. Marten is an old friend of mine. I got these at Nordstrom for forty ducats. "You should go to Gamma Gamma it's a punk rock shop." I should have paid $110? "What kind of drugs have you used?" I never smoked pot. "Why not?" Because the Sex Pistols said, "Don't believe the newspapers and stop smoking pot." I wanted to be anything but a hippie. So did you tweak, fry, zig zag, buzz, hum, x, shoot, swizzle, swagger, pass out puking in gutters of downtown barways? I have used alcohol before, sometimes to excess. "Do you drink and drive?" I have friends who have gone to jail. I am becoming uncomfortably evasive politician manueverizing of bold face change the subject answer prepared safe pabulum answers swerve and curve and spit and hock a logi on the ball so it dips into the batter's eyes dives away from the plate as inedible psychobabble matter of trick false dung chatter strike out.

[Maybe I can speak coach]

If I answer these questions I will never become fully human (I'll be fired.) Yet, the answers are a straight path to
becoming Human, more than being liked, being understood. I think I just entered the Willie *Low*man of the year
contest.[9]

---

[9] Stop right here and reread *Death of a Salesman.* Or just rent the Dustin Hoffman flick
you mindless cow, I'm surprised you've read this far.

sub fourteen

I think I mentioned *the big silence*. A technique. Chris-
tine, another part-time android told me that the young
ones cannot handle silence. "They feed off you." It is true
every time I push air out my gut to address the group, little
lightening clouds of chatter erupt like mice in the walls,
like the amplified sound of a million cockroaches breeding
sparks into the atmosphere. I stop. I remain silent, with the
patience of the Buddha. I can fast, I can wait. I'm getting
paid. Peer pressure sets in, like the ugly sore that it is. I feel
like I'm pimping for the enemy. I am the great preacher of
self control, yet I am paid to slip in a few words edgewise. I
am paid to deliver a vacant lot full of useless thoughts. I always render the first second of silence void with a quick
preach about respect.

I never wanted to be the preacher of the establishment. I did not want to be the great disciplinarian. I'm an anarchist aren't I? I just wanted to turn a few kids on to the ultimate jazz of life. I wanted them to listen, I mean hear with feeling a few of my favorite lines of poetry. I wanted to play a cool tune and watch their toes tap, *and* get them questioning like Socrates. I wanted to see one kid kill her television. Yet, Johnny up-out-of-his-seat-shoot-paper-wads-into-the-basket makes me nervous, and sad like maybe he's missing the point.

I hope I'm not just guided by regret. Why didn't I learn to play saxophone in school, or guitar? Why didn't I read Proust instead of watch *Gilligan's Island* reruns? And all such whiny claptrap fiddle-diddle of zero-motion no action. This is turning into a philosophy book, instead of a book of historical stories, drama moments carefully selected to teach Johnny a lesson. Yuck! (It's also turning into a book aware of itself as a book, and I'm becoming a writer rather than a rider, which strikes me as false, on the outside, sub-human.)

sub fifteen

The referrals. It is archetypal for youngsters to come together if they think a fight is happening. Helix high school.
All I see is fist hit face and (a) hit floor while (b) calls for
more. "Come on punk!" This fight is over. That is my line.
They told me in teacher class that when two guys fight,
neither one really wants to be hurt so they will gladly stop,
if you can get them to hear, 'This fight is over.' Of course
they have to know that it the voice of authority and not
their own chicken conscience squawking.

The very next day, at a school 35 miles away, I see the
same fight, I don't know who pushed who first nor do I
care. This time I will try to empathize, feel their frustra-
tions, give the boxers a break. This fight is over. It works

again. I have the curly-carrot head with glasses askew sit in his seat huff puffing, and I bring the angry one to sit by the teacher's desk with me. I take out a referral, swindle his name from him, write it down. Okay, I won't turn this in if you stay cool for the rest of the day. "Fuck that little punk! That mother fucker!" Okay let's go outside. Luckily there is another teacher passing, an escort to the office. I decide to send the little red head too, maybe they can get some counseling, some aggression reduction therapy, group rate lobotomy.

The next day I'm beat dragging silent tired tuckered spent. I make it to the final period without incident when this kid, Greg (I got his name later) thinks he can do whatever the hell he wants, including one of my personal big no no's: humiliate other students. When he tied the strap of a girl's overalls to her chair, I quietly untied it for her. Ha ha very funny. I don't know what was worse having me untie it or letting her get up and drag the chair across the room. She is public victim clown one, either way. Greg bing bonged from the chair to the lipstick smear campaign. You've already heard about this lipstick caper, and the resulting explosions.

Greg wasn't the first kid to cuss me up and down with his pent-up hostility emissions. I asked a young man, Sam, an eighth grader not to use the teacher's telephone. He said he was talking to his mom, so I reached for the phone. Let me talk to her. "Get your hands off of me mother fucker, or

I'm gonna bomb on you." He was actually snorting like an enraged bull (no stretch, no joke, no blown smoke). Hold on one second while I call the police to haul your ass to jail. Actually I left eleven words out of that statement. There is no truth in the business even in the spontaneous second of adrenal fear. I ended up speaking to his mom. She made him apologize. He stood head down, begrudging the sidewalk out front of the classroom with the toe tip of his shoe. Probably thinking about what a white bread chicken shit asshole I was, or maybe thinking about what his mom picked up at the store in the way of groceries. The sun beat down on our penitent heads with extra heat as to make us aware of the gross wastage of eternity's moments. He was trying to tie his shoes with a stare, and my two evil eyes were trying to lock his eyes in the crushing vice of human to human gaze. There was a human of full tenure with us, a great teacher, a Robin Williams type, Mr. Nubby. He was urging the lad to apologize, make amends, feel remorse, or even to save the moment for a good look back and laugh one day. I hope Sam doesn't end up in prison or dead somewhere without anyone to bury him. I waited until he begrudgingly, did, apologize and then I said, Hey man I don't need your apology, I just want to know that in a similar situation you will try to act more civil, and not put your fist through some poor substitute's nostril. He grunted. I'm not sure what the rest of the class was doing while all this drama filled my conscience. As far as I know they weren't circle-gathered around us in school yard brawl bleachers shouting.

Gompers. Tonya B. globetrotting around the hot day bungalow with a cup of water, dousing some innocent sucker with wet, books wet, papers bleeding, puddle muddling in the slip way. She told me her name was Michelle. I wrote Michelle on the exit visa, please weazling through the greeby cheeks of unmeek streaking. Naked I sent her to room 56, where they keep the rats in face masks. And the torture-keeper is the stoniest faced creature the administration could muster. A medusa of magic guilt inducer, a sonic reducer with stares, and piping down like lead voice for me teacher and student same, it is we who messed up.

Another Gompers' girl gives name game to her lion-toothed and paw clawed tamer and try to beat feet to Market street whore corners and junk doorways. "I don't need an escort, don't touch me with your dirty fingers sub-teacher." So later, I checked her destination and room 56 didn't have her stretched across the rack, or sacking in the thumb screw variation of torture chamber silence. All you can hear in there is the remorseful moans of minds on the grind. So I didn't have her name or face to scan the mug shot books, but I was back the next day waiting, in substitution for her teacher, with pit dug in black ink on the exit slip, just Friday waiting and she came up and asked me to write her a pass out of English class so she could work on some science project. The bold faced audacity of it all. I laughed a big guffaw and the man, the narc, the fuzz, the pig my agent Uncle Tomming at the door. "I don't need no escort." Yes, you do, toodleloo to you.

When most of my exit visas are written for Af-Ams, black skinned beasts of slave times oppression, I stop to wonder. I pull out my racism checker, and bespeckle the situation with critical eye.

I had this kid in class making jungle noises, cricket chirping, monkey whooping, Shere Kaan snarl, and wolf howling, talking not working, distracting everyone around him, inciting riot, lip flap flatulating fart noises that stunk enough to scatter the desk sitters and stomp clatter noise in our reading silence. He was lifting books from their bag holes and putting them in trash cans, using curse language of anger time with silly giggling patter smiles, debasing his fellow mates. I swelled up with the urge to exit him and get on with the plan. Finally I isolated him behind the screen wall of world maps standing. He stuck bunny-fingered puppet hands over and around the sides of his isolation and bleated cow sounds and the pencil I loaned him came rolling out. I stationed myself to stare him down, with my heaviest serious eye. I threw in a bit of remorse around the lip corners. He was tapping on the book beat bongo of tribal rhythm stereotypization. I rode him weary and he slumped off to sleep; the rest of the class read their reading and penciled their fact sheets.

Another time I was bombarded with balled up paper each time I tilted head down to attend the paper shuffle. So I pretended to put my head down, and looked up quintessential quick, catching the little rascal fling flunging on the follow-through. I spot the paper meteor arcing over the planet heads toward my satellite spy. I catch the paper ala Willie Mays cool and drop it calmly into the waste basket. You're outta here buster. "Why?" I say, 'For throwing paper?' With heavy 'You should know' question mark punctuating. "Oh yeah, okay."

I catch kids putting proverbial kick me signs on other kid's backs. I spy with why eyes spit wad shooters and desk top writers. I have to ask children to clean up piles of seed shells saliva sticking to the under the chair floor. I have to say no you can't go to the bathroom when they've just come in from lunch. I have to say no you can't go to the bathroom when I'm giving assignment directions, in the middle of tests, films, group projects, direct instruction lecture time lip flapping of my own didactic ten minute jack-offs. Once a kid said, "I think I have a dookie in my pants can I go check?" Two, three, six, ten to the tenth power times kids have told me they were going to pee themselves.

There is an overall fascination with stupidity which I liken to a society hooked on sports and games, and playing. How else can the utter absolute fixation of five individuals—a mixture of genders, ethnicities and school measured abilities—on a balled-up-piece-of-paper shooter be explained? Three boys rooting and taunting, betting for and or against, and two girls distracted, just gawking, waiting on the edge of their seats to see if the shooter makes his shot. He shoots. Scores, the Bruins take the championship.

sub sixteen

Advanced Placement Biology. Gompers. I taught it for a week, without help of the students who wrote me off as an English major know-nothing of endoplasmic reticulum. My task was to deliver lecture notes and explain the complicated machinery you. I studied the text, and searched out old class notes, searched researched the systems of ATP production—struggled with the info to understand it, yet understanding is two steps behind teaching, which should be more than preaching. I expected them to read the chapters, eleven twelve dig and delve. I wanted us to struggle together, bond, like the most efficient energy maker, fuse, student-subject-teacher triphosphate. Life is metaphor (for me). I am the foolish sighted man among the wise blind women and men.

Clairemont high. Franz of the know everything academic league quizature speaking Russian, German, French, Italian, and Portuguese, but not Spanish with Mexico 40 mile slide down the rain street hiway into the stank sewage of the Tijuana river busting its banks with rank interest. All these languages wasted in the never been anywhere southern California go morning of leafless trees. He was bell ringing with trivia answers to obscure moments, and instantly calculating the ciphers of trains approaching from x distance at y rate. Ding/Answer. Ding/Answer. Ding/Answer.

And another boy same class—a poet writing ten poems a day, and me with no time to read his attention-tattered pencil scrawled notebook of intelligent thinking feeling youth pangs.

Bouvette, everyone calls her Boo Boo, hey Yogi, on her way to being a too smart minor hipshot guru. From Hoover A.P. to the big UCSD studyogomy knowledge injection. Out of the ghetto shelter into the ivy tent of vast googoofizzle. Knowledge Knowledge Knowledge I just wanted to say go keep going, and don't quit and become an auto mechanic like Rupert who once wanted to design engines, or a restaurant manager like his brother (two Japanese genius quitters from way back bogged in Vodka, still trying to get laid on weekends).

Boo Boo sent brother, Singtao, to school in Doctor Marten boots and a bomber jacket. So what? I called him a skin head and we joked about—Japanese supremacy, ha hee. Oh, and I laid the divergent history of the skinhead on him and he was amazed to hear about the black skinheads who started it all in the 1960s Prince Buster proletariat London gig nights. He reads the newspaper too much, convicting all the snarly baldies without proper preliminary political spectrum check.

If only he could dig my pal Shindig (Shindig being locked away in the 16 hour a night work work work of Tokyo) but Shindigger is too deep to fathom, even for me. Him across the sea, dog sled pulling for travel change. Shindig: the mad adventurer, of sad heart three a.m. NINE ONE ONE paramedic hugs. But he's clean and arting up the scenes with ink, and bass slap to flap plap titty plap ditty thud thud, yeahhhgggg! Psychobilly gavel smack on the arm lingering railroad tracks over gravel precisely raked.

sub seventeen

Granite Hills. Another teacher heart failure; my sad task to wish death, or slow recovery on this poor old man I never met. There is a picture of him with some young people, children, his? somebody else's? smiling at any rate. I could fall into his job teaching little lost in the box canyon European emigres. Students all language aligned for my strafing run; I have a week to get wings tacked on my submarine, and fly dangerous hero fodder missions with the recon bullets of good books, and right thinking bombs. Mission: shoot knowledge into the armor skulls of inert bodies. The enemy has been propagandized against me by stifling grammar exorcises. They are entrenched, dug in deep, with slows drugs lows and ugly don't care tanks. My generals, down at the head office, safe behinds behind desk shelter, planning. My generals, here at Granite Hills, have divided the enemy, sorted them into homogeneous intelligence groups. Which I think hoists their morale against my task, it gives them the big-nasty dread weapon: self-fulfilling prophecy. And me terrified by shrill battle yells, "We are the dumb ones!" Meaning we don't have to work as hard. Meaning we've been told we can't, so we can't. It is so easy to be mesmerized by that snake and let it swallow you, Kaa the terrible. It is easy to say you didn't you can't you never will. If you catch me saying that slap me.

The class is reading Helen Keller, and again I seem to be the only one hip to the metaphor, me Annie Sullivan, them spoiled Helen thrashing animal about their own secret world. They are reading parts, Steve, this wild say anything kid, reading with wild India English accents, and real dramatizing which is a snappy refreshment from the usual mono-tono-phono-drono. Yet his shrills and queer volumes are making me queaze and sweat. My innards are gurgling and oozling over with blurp bubbles. The usually notice-everything kids just keep reading, the dozers dozing, the phantisizers flipping across sweet dreams. And the readers reading bleating, and I'm doing narration, with beady perspiration on my brow, and I must be wavering. Or I'm straight okay and the room and time itself is wavering wiggly woo woo. And I still have to stop the play three times for different pairs of kid-oes whisper yakking, or poking each other with those touchy hormone wild fingers of 14.

I'm cool calm bye homework, grab that gum wrapper,
happy Wednesday, aloha, adios. The last student steps out,
and I've got maybe three minutes before the next group
files in for their dose of hi hi's, and page twenty twos, and
who reads who, and sit down and who is gone, absent,
home, safe, in cuddle warm sick bed with the opium hookah on channel 06 numbing the running nose pain of swol-
len heads. Toilet sitting friendly just down the hall.
Whooaa, loop, not me. Trash can, plastic bag (lucky), puke,
vomit, barf, wretch ralph, heave blow chunks that stink up
my nostrils. And I heave again the dulled colors of breakfast liquid streaming into the sack. And I top it off with a
belly wringing painful heave of pure yellow bottom of the
barrel bile. Bllchh. The taste of vomit is in my mouth, nose.
It's in the air. The stench is in the carpet, milling around
the desk. It is a thick haze fog. Maybe it's just a case of
glazed eyeballs, and the dry erase board is not really obscured. I tie up the bag in a big plastic knot. I thank the air
conditioner. I step outside, abandon my breakfast in a blue
steel dumpster, here the stink is just another spice. Flies
shoot up at me, attracted to my breath. I happen upon the
drinking fountain with the cool subterranean nonchalance
of all true hipsters. I bend down to drink. I depress the go
button. The water is welcome. I swirl and spit, all like taking a long thirst quenching drink. It's really just a thorough
mouth douche. I couldn't stomach water. As soon as the
smell is out of my mouth (it would take too long to get it
out of my nostrils) I just stroll into the classroom. I stare at
the trash can ash can bash can, wishing I had another trash

bag. I am weak and woozy. The first student from the next class comes in. I am too sick to smile. She has a big all-the-boys-love-me smile sort of stupid pasted to her pretty little face. I don't go home because I don't want to be gone if the teacher kicks some plastic lined trash bucket of death in whatever hospital they've got him in. I want to be here when the rush panic of now jobs is being thrown out to the lions. I want to be a lion and not a sick little worm, puking and eating my own regretful puke. So I summon up the big teacher voice, for the class go and suffer through the monotony of dramaless play butchering. Only this time I rig things so I don't have to read. I turn the narration reins over to some ms. or mr. helpful in the back row. I just sit on the teacher's desk (high ground is power) and grow nauseous again. Luckily next comes lunch and there is another plastic lined trash can in the teacher's office. Much later I pictured the teacher sort of ponderously musing, "What happened to all my plastic trash bag liners?" He will never know (unless he reads this of course).

sub eighteen

I am the victim (one unready to receive such a gift of great beneficence) of a moment of absolute reverence in the classroom. Absolute audience. There is an unshatterable silence physical-hanging heavy through my senses as if the air had transmuted into a malleable solid. The air is clay. The bodies of this classroom momentarily sculpted into the capital "T" Teacher's classic dream. The perfect audience, receptive GO! For a second I see them as giant ears, sculpted in their chairs by the ghost of Salvador Dali. They await with *absolute* attention (90% beyond normal student functioning attention: fueled by adrenaline.) They burn!— soul-searing, will suffer blistering bubble flesh to know— such is the desire for knowledge at this moment. The silence screaming, "*Tell us!*" I'm not ready. I don't know

enough about the subject—now a sweltering potato juggling on agitated fingertips.

Aaaaaaaaaggghhh! It started with a scream. I hear body
thump. See flash of figure, female, screaming out the door.
Running, I don't see her. She is a streaking model of the
persistence of vision dragging in multiple forms under my
eyelids. Scerpersh. The sound of desk crashing to floor.
Fight? Stabbing? Fellow humans circle. Body seen between
legs.

We had been discussing ghosts, spirits entering the
body. Who believes? Who sceptic? Many unexplainable
things. Voices. I had said, "What if you heard a voice,
sounds like dead relative, says, 'kill your neighbor?'" Luis
says, "I would wait for more info." I say what if the voice
said, I am God-d-d, the voice says if you love me kill your
first born son? The god/devil dilemma. One say "I wouldn't
do it." Some of these kids have children of their own.
"That's a stupid question." I say, It's a big western civilization thing, Old Testament, Abraham, Issac. Then I make
the connection to *Hamlet*. His story we will read over the
next five weeks. Hamlet hears a voice, says kill your uncle,
Now! And I leave the question ponder-hanging in the air
like mist, like mystery, a big unexplainable uncomfortable
thing. Maybe Luis is a natural Hamlet himself. I have the
students writing about their experience with the spirit
world. Ghosts. Almost everyone here believes in ghosts.
Seen photograph with shadowy other-world figure sitting

in should-be-empty chair. Heard ghost trots of 100 years dead three-legged horse at three a.m. Smelled sulphur odor of tumultuous Hell in weird moment. Felt dead sister sitting in room, spirit touching shoulder with cold embrace. The room is charged with this mysterious unexplainable energy.

The body writhing on the floor, I don't even know her name, epilepsy. I am holding the hand of a dead child. Except she will return to life, I know this, I've seen it before, not this close. I am speaking in the ultra-calm *Don't Panic* voice. She is shaking and kicking the desk around. Her limbs are twisted, leg back under body. Slumbering. Me whispering, Everything will be all right. Like holding gunned down body of mother or sister in movie. Inside bone cage I'm sobbing. Face contorted. Hers too, bile froth on lips. She coughs and pushes a little of it out—yellow white spurt. Her soul is out of her body. I can feel it above the crowd. She is crying, knows she will have to return. I back everyone up. Sit. All seated. Nervous tension comes out in giggles, near tears. Inappropriate comments, thinking out of joint, crazy emotional side of brain in control, laughing crying confused. Afterward, all silent, like guilt. The school nurse and some others from outside carry her off, dead weight heavy, shame heavy, left shoe dragging school floor. She rides the wheel chair to a long rest. Save her. Debrief time. All waiting.

"What the hell was that?" Epilepsy. Natural, okay, common. Relax. Five hundred years ago, before the Renaissance, we would have called her possessed by spirits, demons, ghosts (ironic eh?) send for leeches, exorcism. Asylum, lock her away. Hide the unexplainable. What *do* we feel? What do I say to the crowd? The anxious mob, suddenly become one ear. Unified. They are all ears. I can say anything about epilepsy and they will remember it. They want to know. They want there to be talk about it. Even a voice pretending to know something. Give us sound. There should be sound to jam all this empty pain we are feeling. The rest of the day is shot. The plan is banned. Under the spell of trauma all our wheel spinning seems so utterly useless. Life is certainly meaningless. It can be snuffed out in an instance. We feel this now, though it will fade as we shuffle out the door into the big important sea of all our trivialities. Our experience will become gossip, a story passed around, with the truth of raw emotion distilled out every second away from the instant. Meaning and meaningless have switched places so many times in mad moments of raw panic, that we have forgotten which is which. I tell them it takes a hero to go on from here. I have missed my opportunity. The word comes back that she's okay.

sub nineteen

Same epileptic day seizing up on me from all sides. Culture. Don't discriminate against culture. "What is the difference between California and yogurt?" "Yogurt has culture." Groucho buzz word 'A-1' *culture* zing zing ting-a-ling chang chang bop. Not one person in this room can distinguish between Groucho and Karl. Xaythong (known from student teaching days) has had his head ritually shaved in occasion of Lao/Vietnamese New Year. Bald dome of chrome. Bad shave ugly bald lumpy skull. But the rule says 'No hat.' What do ya say Zay? Put that hat on your ridiculous head.

Sixth, last period. Kids poofing white powder on each other. Poof piff. Surprise, fun energy. Piff. Where was it—

zzzt zzzt—when I asked questions about the chapter, the reading? Piff piff. Retaliation with cups of water. Splah ash. Water balloon saved all day, goes down girl's shirt back. Gush ush ush ush ush. This must be a sex ritual. Boy has grin of white powder from ear to chin to elbow to neck to ear. Tooth missing. Girl wring shirt on classroom floor. Shhhhwuuishh. I feel like parent scolding child who wet bed without saying anything. Blaring stare glare. Ancient fertility rite of Spring has sprung. Ung ung ung ung, noise like sprung spring runging.

It is so easy to disrespect culture. Dr. Dorothy Smith (teacher teacher) told me about this CPT thing, Community Potential Time. Colored people's time. An event, class, doesn't start until everybody is there. There are no minute hands in the jungle baby. Bell (grring a ding ding), Charles pass through door, C. sell candy, Me. try to address class with I. instructions, C. bisecting Me. view of class half—pocket packet full of ducats, lips big enough for smiles S., Charles is not ready, therefore class has not begun.

There are cultures that have no built-in respect for a single power head. The council decides. The group, the clan, not the man. No easy biggerest educated man in the classroom thing to overcome. A tribe of know nothings running things you gasp aghast? Guide on the side, slide wide to hide? Somehow I just have to rewrite history from different points of view. Textbooks written by Stinky Cheese Man. We got rid of Columbus that slave trader genocide-artist demon. Let's turn the dirty AIDS infected prison tattoo knife on ourselves. I'm ready bitch! (sorry) We have to make other kinds of experiences valuable. Not easy for my trained brain. And I'm young! A virtual garden of plasticity. I walk around saying I wouldn't sell you two mismatched hip hoots about a dead white male if you paid me in ovaries and testicles and treasure chests full of gold tra la. The DWM's trained me to say that. Like they trained you to whistle cat food commercials. Admit it you're a cow. Moooo. Say mooo for me. Make it audible, especially if you're on a crowded bus, or sitting in an overstuffed coffee house chair. Tell people it's part of your culture. Go fuck yourself, I've had a rotten day.

Why are all these kids running around laughing, chasing flirting, funning up the joint. This is school damn it, NO SMILING HERE. It's part of the culture, vulture.

sub twenty

Kearny High School. Ooo ooo that smell swell that smell pell melter skelter chisel. Clear the room. Point the vicious stinky finger of blame. "Somebody has a gas problem." Sit down, take control of yourselves. Desks scudder away from epicenter clankety ratch hacket jibe in the middle of sub-teacher information sentence. Calm down. "He farted. Mr. X wrote him a referral for farting last week." "Get him outta here." Shoulder shrug smug smile and nod proud. As all eyes focus on him he rips one loose, flplplplplplpth. Oooogghhh! Pandemonium. Kids run out door into the hall.

Hoover High. Deja vu. Smell reeky creeps in from the back of the room. Like baby diarrhea. Everything turns orange-ish light brown. Gaston says, "Ooooggh!" Fingers start to point. "Hey I didn't do it." Sit down relax, it will clear in a second, can we get on with class? Students up standing won't sit down. They pace like puzzled panthers caged with finger pinch nose shut. No exit. Instead of dissipate the smell intensifies. The kids bolt for the doors into the empty echo hall. They begin full volume exclamations, trying to clear the stench out of their sinuses with sound. Come back in here, it's not that bad. Teacher cross hall stick and sic her guilt eye out. Ruff ruff! Kids in the hall— yelling—my responsibility. I force them in. Two or three slip out the other door. In! Pointing finger gestures in virtuoso accompaniment. Classrooms should not have two doors. The smell jumps up three times more stenchful blowing in on the wind. "It's coming from outside." Shut the windows. Shhhhh puuckk. Shut the blinds maybe it won't see us. Control yourselves. "Aaaagh." Still two girls out in the hall. Come in here it's not that bad. One she, Esmerelda, leans over to puke. Pain vibrating on yellow liquid bass string from lip to trash-grey trash can. Bom bom bom. The smell must have jumped into her stomach. Jump right in, jump right out. I return to class. "Okay okay calm down." A saline streak of tear runs from the corner of my irritated eye. All up rove-roaming, afraid to sit. We see people on the campus below (us being on second story) pinching their noses as they cross the quad. We laugh. We laugh as a class laugh, students and teacher all together one-stomach ho ho. This is a big international laugh: Vietnamese, Somali, Eritrean, Mexican, Nicaraguan, Laos, Spaniard, Ugandan, Thai, Mong, Chinese, Japanese, Mira

Mesan chuckle. All laugh except lone girl in hall puking.
We get used to it. Gaston gets used to it first, and someone
says it's because the smell reminds him of home. Was it me
that said that? A few minutes later we hear students from
class across hall exclaiming "Stinks!" in the big echo hall. I
move to the door and see old guilt-eye, "They were blam-
ing it on each other." It's coming from outside. "Oh."

Mr. Smith, v.p., personally delivers rumor control. He
finds "my" class back to work, all seated in crisis time,
thanks be to god. He says, kitchen crew clean the ten grand
gallon grease fat tanks. "Smells like a busted sewer to me,"
I say.

sub twenty-one

Ring skip a beat Ring skip a beat Rang skip a beat Jang skip a beat. Fire drill. Bubbles bubbled already gone. No student roster handy. I don't know anyone in here. Count them. No time. Try to catch sight of a student and follow her. Bodies slipping into the unknown. Look for the emergency plan. "Where do we go?" You're asking me? I've been here fifteen minutes. You've been here six months. The kid who asked me this gone already following the other classes herding outside our window. I can't even remember his face. Stay together. Wait. I think I'm supposed to send a head count to the assistant principal god in charge of fire drills. I will burn for this one. My class, whoever they are, has mingled into a sea of faces, matching face for face the pace race to escape the flame game. I find one girl in a group of girls, gaggling south. I stand next to them and pretend I'm their teacher. The real human teachers look so cool. How do they do it? Crust. Boooooop. No flame to blame. Go back to class. Find the key. Fumble jumble jingle. I drop my key reach over to pick it up. A pen falls out of my shirt pocket followed by thirty seven cents in change, two of them are nickels the other is not how many of them are not quarters? Zzzzzt. I'm not sure, but there seems to be a fewer number of bodies in here. What were we working on? Next period finds fifteen of thirty-four students absent, or should I say nineteen of thirty-four students present.

I find it impossible to keep up with the bureaucratic disaster of details onslaughting whichever desk, podium or table I set up camp on each day. There are spiteful admit cards to be signed, invidious bathroom passes here there. I hate it when a kid brings me an 8.5 x 11 sheet of clean paper to write a pass on. One kid is checking in to class wants a seat, one checking out needs his grade, I don't have it. "Sign this." Check that. There's a kid with a Dead Kennedys T-shirt. I need to tell him about the time I saw them in '85 at the California Theater. No time. I can't find the seating chart. "Do you want our homework?" "Where's Mrs. Whozit?" Go 'way kid ya bother me. Start the lesson at the bell, don't forget the roll call, back track smack jacked whack. Kids getting high on sugar everywhere. Wrappers on the floor.

Many schools have a "nutrition break" with nothing nutritious on the menu. No fruit, no nuts. Just candy soda
chips ripping lips ode ta wired birds flying. The tourist-fed
squirrels of Yosemite are dying of malnutrition. Grip the
clue.

Institution food. Cafeteria grand bland manner. The
only spice they heard of is salt. Ethnic food Tuesday disaster. How can they make rice and beans taste like shit. Yes,
I've tasted shit, smart ass. Yet there is a vegetable quiche,
that savory palate alights delectable! I even heard a French-
man say so. And there is a tomato Florentine soup, which if
you mix enough pepper in, is quite good. Four subs at a
table eating soup, all satisfied. The best thing on the
menu—though it cost you 50 cents—is a peanut square
chew chewy heavy wet sweet peanut yummy on the tum
tum tummy mummy.

sub twenty-two

Monotony is mine. A week later, or was it a week before? Mononucleosussing a monopoly of monogrammed
monotone monogamy, I am still sub-human. If, perchance,
I am assigned to putty up the holes of a teacher not fully
cracked with the burden of classes across Horus' day, then I
must putter away my precious pernicious time filing books
on library shelves, alphabetizing microfiche—a new bard to
guard cards in the lard catalog. Schools not yet computer-
ized their D. Decimal system. Seldom do I shelve an inter-
esting book, which lends me semblance of the rocket
worker bizzy beavering to sweat the job finished. Like cool
hand Luke-savior on the endless tarry asphalt shovel-
morning.[10] I get the whole crew running to kill the labor.

---

[10] I showed *Cool Hand Luke* to an English class one day, but as sub-usual I didn't get to see
the end of the video. We only see the first or last fifty minutes of movies—and we see
those fifty minutes five frigging times a day.

Save one day, I stowed a few glances at some jazz name and picture pages booky little dizzy birds miles, oh Cannonball Adderly where have you taken my jelly roll now? Another time I did a little on-the-clock research of classic cars. I was in the common market way to buy a Ford Falcon, or a Mercury Comet. Wanting more than buying. I like to hear those nostalgic names sounded: Falcon, Bel Air, Fairlane, Meteor, Bessie S my Rainey B Holiday, Ruth Brown move it on down. Though I cannot bear to be just a Gatsby of title shelves. I must hear the melodious sound tuning on my soul fork, and drive the handy rod on the hot road fresh laid. Jump jump, jump to the rhythm and blues. Yeagh heagh!

I spent a Swiss cheese week cross checking lists, counting pencils (2000+) counting test booklets (#23 missing) and answer sheets (bubbling name, birth date, code number and school i.d. for recent add-students.) Recording it all in duplicate. Time in a classroom the holes in that cheese. The counted out material I put in brown grocery sacks. Sometimes 30 sometimes 40 pencils. My discretion. Also 500 calculators, I took each out of its box, checked to see if it worked and marked a big H on its turtle back.

I found one calculator used the year before graffiti stained "Don't fuck with the white boys, just because we fuck with you. S.W.P." I look into the between period passing crowd faces for culprit grin. See no sin. The racist angry scared heartbrain is obscured from me. Me a victim of fish eye, ill equipped to see out of my little thick glass bowl hole. "They all look the same, yes they do."[11] I saw the swastikas painted on garage doors of this community, with the S.W.P. (Supreme White Power I'm told) in dripping white letters.

My dad says our country is reverse racist. 'Why can campuses sponsor all-black, brown, yellow cultural groups, African step club, Latin Roses, Vietnamese Club, but not a white pride group?' Surface-true enough. Dad doesn't see the need for Affirmative Action either. I hear "Brown pride" and "Black pride" every day. "White pride" is a dirty word. The Klan soiled that diaper. Midnight lynchings and poll booth blockade of not so distant history. One day, recent-past class, I read a book[12] about a Chinese immigrant meeting the white "Demons" of San Fran 1909. They did hang Chinamen from lamp posts by their queues. Someday I'll sponsor a group searching for my lost heritage, my Scandinavian gods, food, art, folk tales. They probably eat carcass racks of meat flesh. But I'll have that group meet monthly in a rainbow coalition of culture sharing to shimmy shine America. Yeah. We will learn the African steps and teach them to bury their dead, like ours, on raging funeral pyre. We will feast together on yams, lumpia, molé and whatever my lost food is.

---

[11] Mad Parade *Facing the Crowd*
[12] Laurence Yep *Dragonwings*

I'm putting together the test kits to measure all student-like knowledge. More right, to measure the lack of student-like knowledge. Scarily, I begin to like all this count work. No headaches in the home afternoon. Much energy for daughter play and novel scrawl. We walk to the park swing slide run jump totter on the teeter *and* hop on pop home to write ten pages, *and* stay up till one a.m. reading *The Subterraneans.*

sub twenty-three

I slip out of the groove of teacherism in my count-week isolation, forgetting human interpersonal communication skills. I, called to cover a science class one period, skulk in a corner frightened, unable to address the big imposing group. I wander among them unable to speak any language that they can understand. I become transparent, then invisible. I can see the different bodies milling around work stations, but my proximity control has no effect. They seem to be playing, not working, and I can do nothing to effect their behavior. It is a big classroom set up with rows of work stations. Computers, robot arms, drafting equipment, t.v. video set-ups, audio mixers, hydraulic and pneumatic models. There is a video cart that guides the assembly and disassembly of a small engine. There is a student using the compu-scanner to print out enlarged big booby swimsuit photos, and grainy images of Air Jordan float flying to the hoop jam.

The student is sucking on a cobalt blue pacifier, which dangles from a chain on his neck. His face deadly serious, stone steady, staunch paunch, smileless, but somehow not joyless. Though I might have inserted the snickering evil glint in his eye and the devious flair of his nostrils later. Then I remember my short conversation with his regular teacher. "I have a few students on pacifiers," he said. I thought maybe he meant they lacked maturity. The other pacifier sucking yik yakker is a kind of goofy-wired roaming around the classroom poking pupils and bugging out eyes type. He takes up the bathroom pass swinging it long extended from his arm jolly-like, with a whistle on his breath. He breezes out the door, right past, almost through me like an ethereal wind, without so much as a parting is such sweet sorrow compadré. The aid, a square jawed white-boy-high-on-physics, assures me things will be better with "Baby Huey" (as the other kids called him) outta da picture. Hmm? This aide guy can see me, I think, but as soon as I try to conversate with him he's off leaning over a student, almost touching her long black hair with his square chin, giving advice towards her project. His heavy breath spilling all over her desk. He stepped right out of the grip of my speech, as if I were nothing. I wander a ghost among the rubble of my life, peeling the time from forbidden fruit. Waiting to eat.

I saw see saw hee haw me maw bloody with anticipation. One of the work stations is a tiny room unto itself lodged in the anterior of the class. A pain in the ass. It would be wholly isolate save a large window. In the frame of that large window a student who had been listening head nodding just hanging to a heavy vocal beat rap crunching on the stereo mixture appears. Now he is looking nervously out the window. I also notice that the hard-core pacification mongrel has joined him. The pacifier tries on a shoulder bag for size. It's out of the ordinary bulky, hanging heavy and low on his shoulder. His friend's nervous eyes shoot all around the frame of the glass bing bing bing. I move my wander in the direction of that room. Halfway there I become visible, though still unable to speak, or be heard. I enter the room. Tension. Both snapping lads rap-listening under headphones. They don't even look up. I hold my hand out alms-hungry for the headphones. My own eyes shoot bong bing about the room for clues, anything out of place. What am I looking for? I skull strap the phones, ear vacuum a few hard beats, head-nod and depart. I am more resolved, hence more visible. The aid not only sees me, but seizes upon something wrong in my countenance. I whisper through the corner of my lips for dramatic emphasis, "Pssst. Those two guys back there (behind over my shoulder) are up to something." Brrrangg grrang the bell rangs. I fix a deadly stare on my pacification suspects. In walks Baby Huey against the grain of the crowd rushing out. He had been gone forty-five minutes. Mr. Smooth pacifier #1 rides high on the stream tide. His shoulder bag hanging limp, deflated. We take the small room like marines take a beach. The aide discovers the play/rewind VCR uncorded and out of place aside. "They were trying to steal the VCR," he says, with handful of severed umbilicals dangling. "Last time we had a sub they just stole all the cords and the cables."

If larceny petty thievery pocket heist the lift wise burglar be bop be the theme, let it be supported by numerous examples. Countless full-human-teachers warning "Watch them steal all but the nailed down will for do to you too yip yike hee hee." Levy a syntax on that last sentence. A year before near exacto-knife to the point of the day, Spring break wrapped its urgent pirate flag around the face of sanity, to stranglehold and snuffocate the values of common living. Oh Spring break you necessary demon! Demon I call you, Fie! A pox on your socks cruel fox. The ASB had given the teachers a tiny basket of chocolate eggs. My job was to monitor an ESL class. There were kids in every corner peeping their slick fingers into the cabinets. Finally, yes they did, they stealthed into the teacher's desk and ate his chocolates. Left the aluminum rappings on the floor under his chair. The little basket they left behind on its side, like dead possum. My god what has happened to common human decency? But soft! Me be no stone caster. Coo Coo, "Please pass the ketchup I think I'll go insane." I have lifted enough paper clips and pencils from teacher's desk to stock a charnel house of mirror fun zone mine own. "I've got no values/ nothing to say/ I've got no values/ might as well blow me away."[13]

Corruption certainly starts at the top and seeps into the consciousness of the mass. (I catch myself saying things like this sometimes.)

So the spectrum broadens from what is stolen without shame to what is given without shame. Tom, friend, mathematics teacher, sub, doesn't like math, loves Dostoevsky, and so too believes that 'everything is permitted'—Tom also felt the wrath of Spring break. He was focused on desk work. Grading paper stack of addition and two digit multiplication. He's looking for patterns. Wants to help. Right brain surfing. Gone. Wind conditions, fair, swell pumping. Sudden riding low in the tube. His hand drag skimming on the face of the wave, a smooth woman's face, caressing up up up a jubilant spray of summer and escape America. Tom looks up, right eye left brain, and sees one of his students, his charge, wielding his penis in a girl's face. Naked, bald, ugly. The girl paralyzed with fear, shock horror abomination to the point of humiliation and even sacrilege, verge of hara-kiri. Her lips pursed to burst. There is a scream hiding inside. Eyes glass glazed, beyond seeing, transported somewhere far, across the sea. There was a camp, no water, no family, soldiers brought food. They raped a girl her age in the middle of the night. There was no moon that night. It

---

[13] Black Flag *No Values*

was her. It wasn't her. Tom looks back down at the numbers senselessly scattered on the page. "You look over and you see some guys dick, and your first impulse is to look away. And I'm thinking can I possibly let this one go?" The surf is gone. Beach closed sewage spill. The patterns of error are gone. He will not be able to help Alili with her fractions today. Another day she will slip behind until she is forgotten, lost in the swirling abysmal sea of dada yaya nada. Help is gone. No, no he couldn't possibly let this go and he didn't and it turned out the boy had been grabbing the breastesses and private hypotenuse zones of a whole group of girls for the past week. There is a sexual terrorist in our midst. There is a poster on the wall, missing one tack, curling at the lower left corner. "Don't smoke." New poster needed: "Don't expose your dick." We need a poster for every possible infraction. Take nothing for understood. No chewing blue gum, red gum pink gum bubble gum hum drum gum…No murdering the person in the next seat with knives; No murdering the person in the next seat with guns; No murdering the person in the next seat with battlefield nuclear weapons…napalm, mustard gas, garlic press, inane gibberish, fingers, rubble…No muddering the person in the next seat. No this, no that, no brat a tat a rat a frat grat "Pat sat on bat, No Pat no don't sit on that: cactus."[14] Tom focussed on subject and daydreams rather than protection. Guilt. The girls unable to come forward, dominoes, no English, Vietnamese, culture might blame them.

---

[14] Dr. Suess *Hop on Pop*

Tom and I share the pain, the hilt of the guilt. This is heavy underground man suffering for our kind. My eyelids droop sag as with the weight of little stones. It hurts all stupid in your marrow to have the police come and arrest a kid you were responsible for. They cuffed the little pervert, and collected interpreters and witnesses, and he won't be back. "If only I had made fractions more exciting." Merv the perv will be in someone else's classroom, swerving the nerves, because we solve problems by deck shuffling, luck. Tom will trade his misfortune for someone else's, then he will bang his head against the asphalt and learn to hate his job, because some little punks force you to arrest them. God damn it. Tom will spend the night in jail. Ironic. Hagggh. The kid will go home and watch t.v. Tom isn't equipped to deal with this kid. Neither am I. We cannot win, just suffer, suffer, we might as well suffer: such is the human condition. Are we yet human?

It is more than guilt we feel. I don't know why it should hurt to turn in a criminal. Blame Orwell's *1984*. Despise B. Brother, and despise being used as his agent. Tom is teacher, Tom is agent. But at his core, or in part of his scintillating nature Tom is man, male functioning parts. Hormone driven maniac. Under control of course. Maybe Tom harbored his own sex think towards those girls (something like our young exposer, our flasher in the pan). Perhaps as Tom hands the little indecent wretch over to the cops, Tom turns himself in too. I've had criminal thoughts. Let's face it, I have stolen pencils! Self-penitence too, flagellation with briars, thumbscrews of the mind. Tee hee. I don't know? [Push long contemplative breath out of lungs and stomach so that it makes a rush sound on your lips. Empty yourself. Don't eat for a few days. Rethink Dostoevsky. Stand over an open grave with your back to a Siberian firing squad. Okay, continue.]

The pain here seems more serious than self-betrayal. It seems like part of my culture (a big western civilization thing) that I cannot overthrow—this esteem for the criminal. My roots. At least little grape vine tendrils clinging. I *loooove*-va-va-va-vaa Robin Hood! He and his merry band live and plunder—arrows spling karing bin ping shwooo— in the roots of my hair. Will growing old and bald change that? What about Thoreau sitting in jail? And I will confess here that I love any criminal who steals bread from the fat rich to feed his family. There I said it. I will certainly be precluded from full human employment, but I'll die hungry with a clear conscience. They will cut off my hands. Ha HA hA, whooooo! That feel good! I am free-eeee-eeee-eeeee-eeeee-eeeee-eeeee-eeeee ha ha.

I have found myself looking down on all manner of kids, from pacifier suckers to midnight wall taggers. But it approaches the impossible to look down on them when you think their thoughts, when you see where they are coming from, dig? There was this teachable that I taught in my student teaching days, way yonder. (Student teacher being sub-unpaid-sub-human.) I mentioned him before tagging.

his "Wepon" all over town. I saw "Wepon" on an East Side freeway underpass; Downtown scrawled above Sushi Deli (one of my favorite eat outs); and finally in GIANT letters, color-schemed and bouncy creative, cheering up a tattered billboard in a rusty auto pot hole parking rot and railroad racks erection of town, near the silent daytime Casbah lonely quiet. I talked with him later. He takes pictures of all his exploits. His "crew"—GI (going insane) has their own hats. "Just to know we're causing a little bit of trouble."

Satori in San Diego. Bammo! Struck me like fast train. Looking up at that billboard. These kids, like all who young-think, of yesterday and tomorrow, like Walt Whitman, Zora Hurston, Richard White, Henry Miller,[15] Jack Kerouac, are singing America. Their folly, their art, charged with danger, pissing people off, is part of the Freedom that is America. The land is here to be roamed by man, it's temporary enjoy it. Wepon (like Burn before him) and all the midnight writers are trying to leave a mark. It is art. Even if it be only a stain on the slumland human stain of junk night America.

---

[15] Just started reading *The Air-conditioned Nightmare* which I picked up at the swap meet for 50 cents.

sub twenty-four

Once you've had a *satori* as a sub-human—I mean a
revelation, a true Ah hA peek into the swirling infinite—
where do you go? What's left but to get fat with wisdom
and sadhappy with long grey beard? Surely I could keep
collecting stories, drama bits, mad tales of jest and sad
laughter—for there are as many stories as there are individuals. Here again is the key, the lock, the Dhore of per-
ception, windows like mirrors: *there are no types* (one pacifier sucker is as variant from another as a virgin from a
whore). I had spent my whole life categorizing people,
sorting, labeling. It makes them easy to dismiss, those ideas
you aren't familiar with, right? Phrenology ho! Not for me.
So I will learn to love or hate teachers, administrators, fags,
jocks, environmentalists, women, niggers, gooks, spics,

spud thick mics, butt-kissers, booger pickers, politicians, parents, children, cubists, spokesmodels, hitch-hikers, the news addicted, swing kids, ascetics, ex-cons, average Joes, opium hookah smokers, skaters, sailors, soldiers, surfers, straight edge prohibitionists, cowhands, construction workers, canary owners, indecent Japanese psychobilly bass players, ghetto gangsters, t.v. anchors, cockroaches, retards, young, geeks who attend comic book conventions, old, aids, gigglers, dead white males, intestinal burblers, mathematicians, morticians, pinheads, midgets, men with coarse black hair on their back, women with hair on their back, twenty-first century digital boys, blondes, the famous, the infamous, those neurotically politically correct, deadheads, wops, jews, gigolos, small dogs that pee on your shoes, mail carriers, motorheads, wife, tourists, geniuses, injuns, paupers, poseurs, millionaires, Mormons, bikers, "suburban housewives everywhere with their curlers in their hair,"[16] jazz musicians, Marxists, drunks, alcoholics, writers, taggers, mods, vidiots, shoe salesmen, Iraquis, cootie-coated stink bombs, skinheads, surrealists, crooners, witches, doctors, hippies, punkers, flappers, the MTV generation, pacifists, swallowers, bumper sticker humorists, paramours, patriots, Latin-American women writers of the twenty-first century, grad students, actors, nerds, in-laws, disco dancers, shrinks, waitpersons, obesities, shoppers, friends you never see cause they're married, technical supervisors, supervising technicians, commies, flatulators, japs, whores, cat-lovers, Mr. Jones', neighbor Sams, virgins, all

---

[16] Social Spit *Suburban Society*

night caffeine heads, bible thumpers, brides, bosses, mothers with big lips, revolutionaries, Clash-city chalkers, dope smoking morons, existentialists, food service workers, cardboard tent living raving loons, beat poets, and neo-saint life lovers—each as individual. If only it were that simple.

I can convince myself that it is so simple for a minute and then I'm immersed in work. "Can I go to the bathroom?" "What page?" To be or not to be…[while pondering the question with a class, I just found out that I outlived a former student N.S. R.I.P. (I never got a chance to know him) chose not to be—To sleep perchance to dream…there's the rub!] And I forget because I'm human. I forgot what I forget. I *will* continue to work for eighty-five dollars a day, smile when I hear a student at the classroom door shouting, "A sub a sub!" and rise above the joy or abuse to come. What more do you want?

jazz libs

Jimmy Jazz is _____. He _____ his mother.
                (adjective)   (verb, present tense)

He lives in _____. At the age of _____ he
              (place)   (number)

wrote his first _____. His friends are _____.
              (noun)   (adjective)

He has a _____ daughter who loves to _____.
         (adjective)   (verb, present tense)

He has written two other _____entitled _____
               (noun, plural)   (name)

and _____. The critical acclaim for those
    (name)

_____ was _____. His _____ for punk
(noun, plural)   (adjective)   (emotion)

rock _____ was _____ both to himself and to
     (noun)   (adjective)

those around him. He performs his _____ in front of
                         (noun)

_____ audiences across _____. He has been
(adjective)   (planet)

known to _____ for _____. He thinks you are
       (verb)   (noun)

_____ for buying this book.
(adjective)

" _____ ."
         (what you thought of this book)

—— _____
           (your name)

incommunicado

INCOMMUNICADO PRESS ☆ SAN DIEGO

STEVE ABEE ☆ KING PLANET 145 pages, $12.

DAVE ALVIN ☆ ANY ROUGH TIMES ARE NOW BEHIND YOU 164 pages, $12.

ELISABETH A. BELILE ☆ POLISHING THE BAYONET 150 pages, $12.

IRIS BERRY ☆ TWO BLOCKS EAST OF VINE 108 pages, $11.

BETH BORRUS ☆ FAST DIVORCE BANKRUPTCY 142 pages, $12.

PLEASANT GEHMAN ☆ PRINCESS OF HOLLYWOOD 152 pages, $12.

PLEASANT GEHMAN ☆ SEÑORITA SIN 110 pages, $11.

R. COLE HEINOWITZ ☆ DAILY CHIMERA 124 pages, $12.

HELL ON WHEELS ☆ ED. BY GREG JACOBS 148 pages, $15.

JIMMY JAZZ ☆ THE SUB 108 pages, $11.

NICOLE PANTER ☆ MR. RIGHT ON AND OTHER STORIES 110 pages, $11.

PETER PLATE ☆ ONE FOOT OFF THE GUTTER 200 pages, $13.

UNNATURAL DISASTERS ☆ ED. BY NICOLE PANTER 240 pages, $15.

☆ SPOKEN WORD CDS: GYNOMITE—FEARLESS FEMINIST PORN, $14.
EXPLODED VIEWS—A SAN DIEGO SPOKEN WORD COMPILATION, $14.

☆ COMING SOON:

SCREAM WHEN YOU BURN ☆ ED. BY ROB COHEN (September, 1996)

DAHLIA & RUDE ☆ ARMED TO THE TEETH WITH LIPSTICK (October, 1996)

PETER PLATE ☆ SNITCH FACTORY (November, 1996)

AVAILABLE AT BOOKSTORES NATIONALLY OR ORDER DIRECT: INCOMMUNICADO, P.O. BOX 99090 SAN DIEGO CA 92169. INCLUDE $3 SHIPPING FOR 1,2, OR 3 ITEMS, $5 FOR 4 OR MORE. MAKE CHECKS PAYABLE TO ROCKPRESS. WRITE FOR FREE CATALOG OR VISIT OUR WEBSITE: http://www.tumyeto.com/incom/ DISTRIBUTED TO THE TRADE BY CONSORTIUM BOOK SALES.